GIANT EDITIONS

OUT OF THE AFRICAN ARK

EDITED BY DAVID AND GUY BUTLER

With zoological descriptions by
CARMEN WELZ

AD. DONKER / PUBLISHER

AD. DONKER (PTY) LTD
A subsidiary of Donker Holdings (Pty) Ltd
PO Box 41021
Craighall
2024

First published 1988

ISBN 0 86852 147 7 (paperback)
ISBN 0 86852 148 5 (hardback)

Typeset by Industrial Graphics (Pty) Ltd, Johannesburg
Printed and bound by National Book Printers,
Goodwood, Cape.

Contents

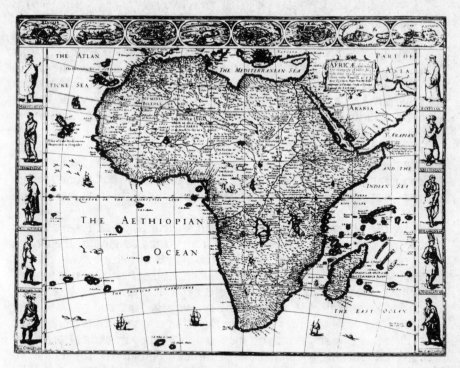

Introduction: Ex Africa

No other continent is as rich in animal varieties as Africa. Roy Campbell was taking a legitimate poetic licence when in *The Flaming Terrapin*, he made his Noah beach the ark in the heart of this enormous and varied land mass. The glory of the animal kingdom spills from confinement:

> Out of the ark's grim hold
> A torrent of splendour rolled -
> From the hollow resounding sides,
> Flashing and glittering, came
> Panthers with sparkled hides,
> And tigers scribbled with flame,
> And lions in grisly trains
> Cascading their golden manes.
> They romped in the morning light,
> And over their stripes and stars
> The sun shot lightnings, quivering bright
> Rippled in zigzag bars ...

Africa's cornucopia of beautiful and energetic beasts was known to the ancient civilisations of Europe, Asia Minor and the Far East. Cleopatra is called 'my serpent of old Nile' by her lover Antony; and Romans returning from Africa were catechised about the strange beasts there, such as the crocodile. Roman crowds marvelled at the wealth of animals (not only hungry lions) which Africa produced for the circus. The continent became known as an apparently inexhaustible supply of new wonders: *Ex Africa semper aliquid novi*, said Pliny the Elder.

The princes of India and China were no less intrigued. In the early fifteenth century the Emperor of all the Chinas was delighted and puzzled by a splendid African giraffe which the talent scouts of his menagerie had found for him in India - a staging post to China. A painting on silk of this elegant creature and its troubled groom has survived.

Among the Kings of Egypt there was an ancient tradition (as old as the Pharaohs?) of sending strange animals from Africa as gifts to their regal brothers - animals which had travelled thousands of miles by water down the Nile. So in 1825 the governor of the Sudan, Muker Bey, sent two giraffes as a gift to Muhammad Ali, viceroy of Egypt. The great Pasha sent one to Charles X of France. It had an easy sea voyage, but had to walk from Marseilles to Paris - together with two Egyptian cows which provided milk for its diet. Stage by stage, interest mounted to a happy hysteria. The animal was given a touching triumphal march through Paris to the royal chateau of St. Cloud. 'Plume-bedecked generals led the way and troops from the garrison of Paris lined the route; ermine-clad notables vied for attention with officials in medals and decorations, and the mace-bearers of the faculties sweated under the weight of their insignia of office.' Finally the King of France profered his new subject rose-petals from his own hand. After this audience she was housed in a specially heated apartment in the *Jardin de Plantes*. Within six months, more than half a million Parisians had visited her. She died peacefully in 1845. (See George Poisson *A Giraffe for the King, UNESCO Courier,* March 1986.)

About the same time, Muhammed Ali Pasha, with fine diplomatic impartiality, sent another giraffe to the King of England, George IV, who kept it in the Royal Menageries (which on his death formed the nucleus of the London zoo.) The King's collection included gnus, kangaroos, and a vast collection of rare birds; but his greatest prize was the young Nubian giraffe, whose beauty entranced him. Nothing could give an idea of the beauty of her eyes. One of his last commissions was a picture of the giraffe by Agasse (1827). The beast did not live long, however. The English climate (or its quarters?) being colder than the French, it died after two years, to be followed shortly by the monarch who was haunted by its beauty. (See Huw Weldon and J.H. Plumb, *Royal Heritage*, London: Chancellor Press, 1984, p.240.)

14

African animals are now scattered in zoos and game parks throughout the world. Certain threatened species may have a better chance of survival outside Africa than in. The eland was taken to the steppes of Central Asia in the late nineteenth century; herds of rhinoceros have been established in suitable habitats in the United States. Our animal exports, whether to game parks, circuses or zoos, have long been a source of wonder, delight and amusement.

The power of animals to capture the imagination is well recognized. For many reasons, they have fascinated and preoccupied artists of all kinds throughout the various stages of man's development.

This book is a collection of animal trophies created by culturally and historically diverse artists; trophies where the essence of the animal is stalked and captured from as many different angles and for as many different reasons as possible. We have presented images from those who hunted for food and clothing; those who hunted for sport; those who hunted for the joy of killing, and those who sought to conserve. There are those who are familiar with the animals, and those to whom they are totally strange. Some see the animal as an index to the wisdom and glory of God; others use the animals to satirize man's vices or praise his virtues; others try to see each animal in its wonderful uniqueness.

The Nature of Nature - The Pyramid of Life

Nature is a very intricate and dynamic process, a never ending cycle of birth, feeding, growth, mating, rearing of young, decline, death, and decay. The broad foundation of what has been described as the pyramid of life is earth's thin coating of topsoil, which, given moisture from the clouds and warmth from the sun, produces the great vegetable coat of many colours, changing with the changing seasons; ranging from desert xerophytes, through grasslands and savannahs, to forests and mountain uplands. Each of these zones has its characteristic population of animals, which can be conveniently divided into three main classes.

Herbivores or Vegetarians

By far the largest groups are the vegetarians, or herbivores, eaters of grass and leaves. All the antelopes, from the dainty duiker to the enormous eland; the camouflaged relatives of the horse, the bizarre giraffe and the dazzling zebra; those enormous, adipose oddities, the rhino, the hippo and the elephant, and many others. As they have to consume great quantities of

16

greens to produce a very little protein, these vegetarians spend their lives endlessly eating. They are always in danger of being eaten themselves: so they are variously equipped with speed, camouflage, or horns; or, occasionally, spines, like the gentle porcupine; or they are simply too big for even a lion to tackle. A full grown elephant could squash the king of the beasts with a foot, or roll the breath out of him.

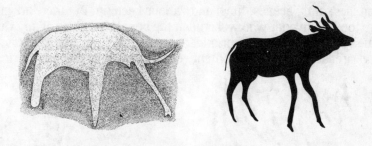

Carnivores or Predators

The meat eaters, or carnivores, are a very different breed. They kill and eat the vegetarians. Having made a good meal of pure protein (buck, zebra, giraffe) they can lounge and drowse in a benign digestive daze for days on end, until hunger makes them lethal once more. (See 'Cheetah' by Eglington.) They are perhaps, as a group, the most beautiful family among the mammals: the lion, the leopard, the cheetah, the wild cat.

Reptiles make less attractive predators - the crocodile, the puff-adder and the chameleon look what they are, stealthy, sinister creatures incapable of displaying the kittenish charm of the cats, big or small. Among the birds the predatory eagle is most beautiful to behold, except at meal times.

As always, there are charming oddities. What could look less like a predator than the toothless aardvark? A huge mobile potato with a carrot snout, this shy shambler has survived on a special diet of ants.

17

Decomposers

But, like the herbivores, the carnivores also have to die. As animals do not bury their dead nature has to dispose of them somehow, to save the whole world from being cluttered up with corpses! Lifeless bodies simply have to be reduced to the earth and the useful chemicals from which they were made. Decomposers are essential to the cycle, the most notable being carrion flies, ants, beetles, fungi and various bacteria. But there are grander agents too: the hyena, who will crunch the bones and hides of any carcass; and the vulture, lovely in flight, hideous and smelly at close quarters. Also, several predators are quite content, occasionally, to feed on carrion.

Zoological Classification

There are, of course, other ways of classifying animals: not by diet, but by physiology.

Arthropods

The most primitive creatures in this book are the arthropods - the ant, spider, scorpion, dragonfly, mantis and carpenter bee, between whom and the rest of our animals the main difference seems to be their structure - their 'bones' are on the surface, not inside their flesh. They too, like the reptiles and the mammals, range from vegetarians, to predators, to decomposers.

Amphibians

We have included no cold-blooded fish: the nearest is the amphibious frog, a comic looking predator, a lion of the mud.

Reptiles

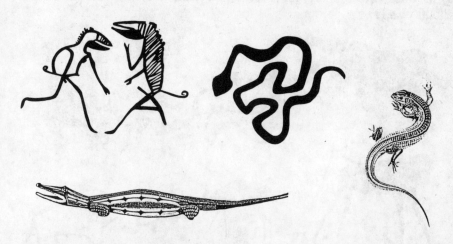

Of the reptiles we have the ageless vegetarian tortoise; the predatory crocodile, who is also a scavenger (who 'purifies the river'); the well-camouflaged
lizard and chameleon, the slender cobra, and the sudden puff-adder.

Birds

As for the birds, (which deserve a book of poems to themselves) we have
included only four of the most striking: the ostrich, the guinea fowl, the
eagle, and the vulture, the first two being vegetarians, the third a predator,
the fourth a decomposer.

By far the greatest family, however, is the warmblooded mammals - 27 of a total of 44.

Mythical Beasts

Of these we have introduced only two, the ugly Yahoo and the beautiful Unicorn.

Alphabet

In presenting our selection, we have followed an alphabetical index. Thus the less popular animal subjects such as the antbear, hyena, nagapie etc., which would otherwise have been swamped by the many excellent poems about their more majestic neighbours (elephant, lion, buffalo, etc.) get a look in as well. It has also resulted in a more rounded overall picture of the animal kingdom, with representatives of carnivores and herbivores, as well as the less glamorous but equally wonderful decomposers. We could find no obvious animals for Q, U, X and Y and had to use our ingenuity.

Pictures

The animals selected have been illustrated by various African artists, and once again our concern has been to present a wide range of artistic perceptions. Where possible, we have included an image of each of the animals by that greatest school of South African painters, the Bushmen. There are drawings by 'European' artists from Thomas Baines through to Cecil Skotnes and beyond, as well as contemporary African woodcarvings and line-cuts.

Zoological Notes

The objective existence of the living creatures suggested by the pictures is supported by brief scientific notes by Carmen Wels on its distribution, diet and habits.

The Poems

The main approach of the book is through poetry. The poems, dating from Thomas Pringle through to Douglas Livingstone and beyond, are not exclusively by South African poets, nor have we selected poems written only in English: we have included several Afrikaans, Sotho and Shona poems in English translations.

Proverbs and Folktales

We have also included examples of African proverbs in which our chosen animals appear. These concise statements, translated from their original

Zulu, Xhosa and Shona, together with some examples of Bushman animal myths, are evidence of a time when animals were not confined to poetry, reserves and zoos, but, because of their abundance and proximity, permeated everyday language and imagination.

It is our hope that a boldly silhouetted image of the animal, coupled with the pungent African proverb, will enrich the reading of the poem. Frequently the reader will be contemplating an animal through lenses provided by three different cultural sources: Bushman, African, and 'Western'.

This book is not concerned with domestic animals. Man's long and complex alliance with sheep, goats, cattle, horses, poultry, cats and dogs is a great topic, but not our concern. We are interested in the wild creature, untainted by man, still unbroken to his will, surviving in the waste places and deserts; or in game parks, those small areas of the earth which man has set aside to conserve portions of nature which he would otherwise obliterate. Except in two cases, we have avoided animals in zoos.

Some attempt has been made to balance the anthology in respect of the humorous and the serious. This has not been too difficult because the incredible diversity and ingenuity of nature has produced animals combining the weird, comic and exotic as well as the graceful, majestic and powerful.

Man and the Animals

Much has happened to the world and Africa since the animals poured out of the ark. It now seems indisuptable that it was in the heart of this continent that one species of primates, having learnt to make tools and weapons, set out to conquer, terrorise, and destroy much of the natural order in which he once filled a fairly innocuous niche. One of the secrets of his impressive and appalling success was the nature of his appetite. Most other creatures tend to be fussy specialists in their diets. Man is an omnivorous creature: he has always liked both meat and veg; and he has become so efficient at securing them that he now poses a threat to all other forms of life on earth.

22

Bushmen - Man in Balance with Nature

In Africa we can still glimpse in the Bushmen and in their pictorial legacy, what early man was like and how he lived when his weapons were bone and stone, when the women gathered bulbs and seeds in the veld and the men hunted the beasts, big and small, with difficulty and great skill. Few in numbers, man then posed no threat to the natural order. He was not only a patient and cunning hunter employing camouflage, (see the Ostrich painting) but a superlative animal artist, hunting his victim with eye and skilful hand, whether the hand guided the arrow or the brush (see 'Eland' by Wilma Stockenström).

Bushman rock art had caught the attention - and imagination - of most travellers in the eighteenth and nineteenth centuries. Thus Pringle in 'The Emigrant's Cabin' took note of a gallery of their paintings:

> Beside the Krantz whose pictured records told
> Of Bushman paintings in the days of old.

Thomas Baines, a great animal painter, found his way to the same spot in 1849, and to several other Bushman sites.

Proceeded to the Bushman's Krantz... After sketching the general scene I made facsimiles of the various figures in colour. Among the most prominent were the buffalo, camelopard, hartebeeste, and a thing that by a stretch of imagination might be fancied into a unicorn, but I could find no decided representation of one, and considering the accuracy with which all other animals are drawn I should like to see something less equivocal before I assert on my own authority that the unicorn is painted in the Bushman's cave. A clear definition of a one-horned animal on one of these rocks would be a strong confirmation of the existence of such a creature, for they give every two-horned animal two horns. One figure represented a Bushman equipped for war, with arrows stuck in a fillet around his head like those in Daniell's print, another was a Bushman shooting, and one a baboon. (p.167 Thomas Baines: *Journal of Residence in Africa* ed. R.F. Kennedy, Cape Town VRS. 1961, Vol.1.)

But the first person to make a major contribution to copying, recording and studying our wonderful legacy of rock art was G.W. Stow, several of whose copies are included in this work, such as ostriches.

In Bushman cosmology man and the animals are part of a single order. Much of his folklore accounts for the present enmity between the members of the single man-animal family as caused by unfortunate quarrels in the past. (See 'The Lioness and the Children' and 'The Woman who was a sister to Vultures'). There is little distinction between sacred and secular in their awareness of life.

Pastoralists

This African stone-age hunter-gatherer has had to give way before black settlers coming overland from the north, and later, white sea-borne settlers from the south. Both the newcomers were pastoralists and agriculturalists, for whom hunting and gathering was a secondary activity. These peoples depended on domesticated animals and on crops. Neither understood nor loved the wild animals as the Bushmen did. And neither Black nor White pastoralists showed much tolerance towards the nomadic hunters and gatherers, and for a very simple reason. Flocks and herds drove the game away from the hunting grounds of the ancient people, who had little option but to steal the cattle and sheep of the invaders of their ancient hunting grounds.

If the Black and White pastoralists were very different from the Bushmen, they also differed greatly from each other.

There were things the white man brought with him which determined his relationship to all other forms of life in Africa, human or animal: the horse, the gun, the plough; and behind these came the merino sheep, the angora goat, maize, sugar-cane and a host of other exotic animals and plants which have conquered and destroyed much of the ancient ecology of Africa.

First, a brief glance at the relationship between men and wild animals in African pastoral society.

The African relationship with the animal world is very different from the Bushman, and, of course, varies from tribe to tribe. Here is a glimpse of the familiarity with animals that existed in Xhosa society of the South Eastern Cape in the early years of the last century, when a roll-call of the Ark would have shown 'all present and correct'.

Stephen Kay lists elephant, rhinoceros, hippopotamus, lion, leopard, zebra, jackal, hyena, many kinds of buck, and game birds. Skins of lion and leopard, and hide and tusks of lephant, rhinocerous and hippo were the prerequisites of chiefs, and among the southern chiefdoms the chief's capital was marked by an elephant's tail attached to the pole. Throughout the area the symbol of executive authority was the leopard's tail attached to a spear, carried by the court messenger. (W.O. Hammond-Tooke, 'Symbolic structure of Cape Ngumi Cosmology', in *Religion and Social Change in Southern Africa*, 1975, p. 23).

For the Xhosa there are three broad categories of animals: flesh eaters (carnivores), edible wild animals (antelopes), and domestic animals, each of which has its favourite habitat. The carnivores (like Blake's *Tyger*) live in the forest, a place of awe and danger; the antelopes live in the grassland, and the domestic animals round the homestead. The domestic beasts are the life of the people. Men and cattle live in a symbiotic relationship, and much fine African poetry springs from this source.

Although African poems about wild animals in isolation are rare, animal images abound in poetry. In their great 'praises' the chiefs are endowed by metaphor and simile with all the virtues — the power, speed, beauty, death-dealing and life-giving — of the animals.

The impact of such images gained enormously in the traditional dramatic presentation of the praise. Cornwallis Harris gives us a vivid account of the animal miming that accompanied the words:

... a herald, called in the Matabele language, Imbongo, a proclaimer of the king's titles, suddenly made his appearance outside the kraal, to give us a little insight into His Majesty's biography. Advancing slowly towards the waggons, he opened the exhibition by roaring and charging, in frantic imitation of the king of beasts — then placing his arm before his mouth, and swinging it rapidly in pantomime representation of the elephant, he threw his trunk above his head and shrilly trumpeted. He next ran on tiptoe imitating the ostrich; and lastly, humbling himself into the dust, wept like an infant. At each interval of the scene, he recounted the matchless prowess and mighty conquests of his illustrious monarch, and made the hills re-echo with his praise. (p.96 W. Cornwallis Harris *Wild Sports of Southern Africa*, London 1852.)

If African poems devoted specifically to wild animals are rare (but see 'The Clan Praises of Chikota's Clan' for the Zebra, and the Sotho 'Leopard'), African proverbs abound in them; and, like proverbs generally, they can pack a fine, memorable punch. A ghostly, rapidly disappearing animal kingdom still survives in countless African sayings. One hopes that proper conservation, with grassroots support, will restore these fading beasts to the eyes of the people who now know them as proverbs only.

Aesop is alive and well ...

And not only in proverbs, which form a major element in this book, but in fables. Indeed, the fables of Aesop are still alive in Africa, where they originated. Certain beasts are given a character, or qualities, which can be neatly transferred to man. This wealth of saying, clearly derives from a time when men and animals were familiar with each other in a way which eldom occurs today. Abraham Kriel (*An African Horizon*) devotes a fascinating chapter (p.47-79) to animal symbols among the Shona. Our poem about the *Xylocopa* (Carpenter Bee) and *Pimbirimano* owes its origin to Kriel's account of this insect. (p.78) The following paragraph, although written about the maShona, is generally applicable in Southern Africa.

In animal stories the maShona show which powers they would *want to* be victorious. Animals have been equated with referents as follows:

Baboon = stupidity, theft
Hyena = desire, lust, greed, magic
Lion = authority, order, tradition
Elephant = muscular power
Hare = cleverness, planning
Tortoise = righteousness and profound wisdom.

Stupidity and theft, naturally, lead to nothing, and no achievements can be expected of a baboon, whose chief function is that of a symbol providing enjoyment by being rejected. It is also found that muscular power and brute strength fail to achieve much, and can be manipulated to neutralise themselves as in a tug-of-war. Elephant never defeats any other animal. Nor does Hyena, the symbol of desire, who is traditionally the servant of Lion, as he should be, for if desire is not controled by authori-

ty and tradition, where would we all be? Lion, the symbol of authority, would forever maintain the status quo, seeing to it that his own wants are satisfied, but also curbing the inordinate passion of hyena in the interests of the community. This does not satisfy the Hare, who is romantic enouth to desire change, and clever enough to contrive it but not wise enough to see the results of such actions. All this is very exciting and stimulating, but no society can bear it in unrestricted form. There is need for someone to correct it, even at the risk of gaining the reputation of being unsightly. This is where Tortoise comes in, the representative of righteousness and deep insight into the wider context of actions, the small but hardy symbol of the conscience which speaks up when it is least expected and most unwelcome, but which nevertheless saves the others in the moment of acute crisis, when it is impossible for tradition in the form of Lion, or brute strength in the form of Elephant to curb the awakened intellect in the form of Hare. Who knows but that the maShona feel just a bit guilty at enjoying the unscrupulous escapades of Hare, and make amends for this by introducing Tortoise to cast the final verdict? (p.79)

The Gentleman with Horse and Gun, the Destroyer of the Balance of Nature

Nothing can stand before this armed, mounted man. He clears the country to make it safe for his family, his animals and plants. Anything that dares to kill or eat what he has tamed to kill and eat himself, becomes vermin. He hunts and traps the predators or whatever raids his crops (as in Kingsley Fairbridge's 'Yellow Eyes' and 'Bongwi the Baboon'). Further, he does not only hunt for these practical reasons: he hunts because he enjoys hunting.

Between the Bushmen who hunted for food and the gentlemen who hunted for sport there is an enormous difference. Food has become game; the chances of the beasts are reduced by man's animal ally, the fleet-footed horse; and by civilisation's characteristic gift, firearms, so much more efficient than the bow and arrow. Here is a description of one of the most civilised of the hunters at work — Cornwallis Harris, whose pencil left a superb and loving record of the beasts he killed. The paradox of the hunter/victim has seldom been better demonstrated than in his account of killing a giraffe:

> The stately bull, being readily distinguishable from the rest by his dark chestnut robe, and superior stature, I applied the muzzle of my rifle behind his dappled shoulder, with the right hand, and drew both triggers; but he still continued to shuffle along, and being afraid of losing him, should I dismount, among the extensive mimosa groves, with which the landscape was now obscured, I sat in my saddle, loading and firing behind the elbow, and then placing myself across his path, until, the tears

trickling from his full brilliant eye, his lofty frame began to totter and at the seventeenth discharge from the deadly grooved bore, like a falling minaret bowing his graceful head from the skies, his proud form was prostrate in the dust. Never shall I forget the tingling excitement of the moment. At last then the summit of my hunting ambition was actually attained, and the towering giraffe laid low. Tossing my turbanless cap into the air, alone, in the wild wood, I hurrahed with bursting exultation, and unsaddling my steed, sank exhausted beside the noble prize I had won. (p.197 W. Cornwallis Harris, *Wild Sports of Southern Africa*, London, 1852).

The killing of giraffes — because of their towering height? — seems to give hunters more satsfaction than other deaths they inflict. Here is another famous hunter, 'who rode ... in the kilt with my arms bare to the shoulders', Roualeyn Gordon Cumming, killing his first camelopard:

In a few minutes I was riding within five yards of her stern, and, firing at the gallop, sent a bullet into her back; increasing my pace, I next rode alongside, and, placing the muzzle of my rifle within a few feet of her, fired my second shot behind the shoulder - the ball, however, seemed to have little effect. I then placed myself directly in front, when she came to a walk, and dismounting, I hastily loaded both barrels, putting in a double charge of powder; but before I was ready she was off at a canter. In a short time I brought her to a stand at fifteen yards in the dry bed of a watercourse, and fired, aiming where I thought her heart lay, upon which she again started; having reloaded, I followed, and had very nearly lost her, for she turned abruptly to the left, and was far out of sight, among the trees. Once more I brought her to a stand, and dismounting, gazed in wonder at her extreme beauty, while her soft dark eye, with its silky fringe, looked down imploringly at me: I really felt a pang of sorrow in this moment of triumph for the blood I was shedding; but the sporting feeling prevailed, and pointing my rifle towards the skies, I sent a bullet through her neck. On receiving it, she reared high on her hind legs and fell backwards with a heavy crash, making the earth shake around her — a thick stream of dark blood spouted far from the wound, her colossal limbs quivered for a moment, and she expired. (R.G. Cumming, *Five Years' Adventures in the Far Interior of South Africa*, London: John Murray, 1873, p.160-1).

Royal Hunts

But the spectacle of the individual hunter at work pales before the 'drives' of game by beaters, which the great African chiefs organised. Once he had established himself in the Transvaal, Moselekatse enjoyed royal hunts. W. Cornwallis Harris devotes some space to describing them:

On these occasions, remnants of the conquered nations being expressly assembled, he is attended by a retinue of several thousand vassals, who, extending themselves in a circle, enclose many square miles of country, and gradually converge so as to bring incredible numbers of wild animals within small focus. Still advancing, the ring at length becomes a thick and continuous line of men, hemming in the game on all sides, which in desperate efforts to escape, display the most daring and dangerous exhibition of sport that can be conceived. As the scene closes the spears of the warriors deal death around them, affording a picture, thrilling to the sportsman, and striking in the extreme.

So striking that it inspires Harris to not very good epic verse:

... Deep in his gloomy lair
The lion starts, and morsels yet unchewed
Drop from his trembling jaws. The shouts
Of eager hosts through all the circling line,
And the wild howlings of the beasts within
Rend wide the welkin. Pressed on,

At length within the narrow plain confined,
A listed field marked out for bloody deeds,
An amphitheatre more glorious far
Than ancient Rome could boast, they crowd in heaps
Dismayed and quite appalled. Flights of arrows, winged
With death, and javelins launched from every arm
Gall sore the brutal band, with many a wound
Gored through and through ...
... With pointed spears men pierce
Through their tough hides, or at their gaping mouths
The easier passage find. The king of brutes
In broken roarings breathes his last ...
(W. Cornwallis Harris, *Wild Animals of Southern Africa*, London, 1840,
p.35)

In 1860 a similar hunt — but with the deadly addition of firearms and horses
— was organised for the first British Prince to cross the equator, the ill-fated
Alfred. It took place on Mr Bain's farm 'Hartebeeshoek' near Bloemfon-
tein. The beaters were eight hundred Barolong, all mounted and armed, under
the control of Moroko's son. The quantity of game shut in by the Barolongs
was estimated at from twenty to thirty thousand:

32

The herds of animals could be seen rushing in wild confusion at full gallop along the living cordon which enclosed them. As it gradually closed in and drew nearer and nearer, the game grew more and more frantic with terror. Fiercer and more determined rushes were made by the maddened animals upon the line — more and more of them were shot down or killed by assegais — but no Barolong stopped to lift what he had killed. Flocks of vultures, delighting in the slaughter, hovered round, and sometimes pitched on the ground quite close to the hunters.

Thus swept on this great moving mass of life. As the circle still contracted, the droves of game formed into larger masses and, at last, reckless apparently of death and wounds, broke through the drivers in numerous bodies, so that when the whole mass swept past Mr Bain's house into the narrow valley down which we had ridden to the farm, probably not more than three thousand head of game of all kinds remained enclosed by the hunters.

The dismounted men who had been ranged along the slopes of the hills in this valley, now rose up — the game was fairly surrounded by a mass of men — the Prince's party moved on with the hunters, rather in advance of the line — pop, pop went guns and rifles in all directions — down fell game on this side and that side — in every direction flew assegais; with these sticking in them many of the wounded animals galloped about, so that, as was said at the time, you might compare them to inkstands with pens sticking in them. Balls from one side or the other passed unpleasantly near you. The greedy vultures, knowing they were safe, pitched, in some cases, immediately in front on the hunters, stalked on before them, and could hardly be made to rise.

Still, in this way, all but the animals who were slain moved on to the range of hills down which we had come into the valley, and also on which stood the line of men who had been first placed there. Here and there small droves of game would break through the gradually closing line — in other places the animals worn out by their exertions to escape, stood in small bodies hardly able to move, and scarcely seeking to evade their destroyers, who, with shouts, cries and discharges of fire-arms, were each moment shutting them into a narrower and narrower circle.

The Prince, up to this point of the hunt, had shot about twenty-five head of large game to his own gun, and joined in all the excitement of the fray with cordial enthusiasm. The grave Sir George Grey and the dignified Major Cowell forgot their dignity and their gravity, and grew young again in the hot pursuit of the flying game; while the dashing Sir Walter Currie went at it all coatless, hogspear in hand. Even the ladies who joined the party laid aside their natural timidity, and shared the excitement of the occasion as thoroughly and as amusingly as the rest'' (*The Progress of Prince Alfred through South Africa 1860*, Cape Town: Saul Solomon, 1861).

The exploits of individual hunters or organised hunts found a ready relationship in the 19th century. High class picturesque hunts still survive in some civilised parts of the world; but it does seem that there has been a significant swing in public opinion against blood sports. Descriptions of mass slaughter, which aimed at admiration, now have the opposite effect.

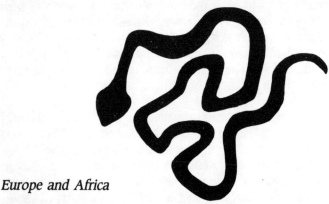

Europe and Africa

The mighty European conquerors fell victim to the vanity of all conquerors. Assuming that their economic power, superior weaponry and more advanced science gave them the moral and intellectual freedom of the world, they regarded other continents as exciting places to be explored, exploited, and ransacked for treasures. Nature for many was a source of animal trophies either for natural history collections or to grace the halls of the gentry. They had little humility or insight. Sydney Clouts's 'Salute' says much on this score with witty concision. For the 'Very Profound Men' of Europe the rest of the globe was a source of amusement, worthy of indulgent curiosity.

> On the world's perimeters, sharksfins, anteaters,
> kangaroo, pearl oysters, bears
> and others (fit for smiles).

But for the rest of the world

> It was the Wolf of Europe that went prowling.

Some of the courtesies of the Wolf, however, betray his abysmal ignorance:

> 'Good morning, gentle cobra, are you well?'

34

Once man becomes complete master he begins to show an equivocal mercy on what is at his mercy. Mingled with the killing instinct he has always shown a love or admiration for his victims, for their speed, beauty, courage, strength or cunning. This love of the brute creation was encouraged by the great eighteenth and nineteenth century growth in the biological sciences, a new reverence for life, which the Romantic movement encouraged. 'Everything that lives is holy' said Blake. Aesthetic awareness of the beauty of creatures grew. Francois le Vaillant and Cornwallis Harris are good examples of early artist-hunters. Europe produced a host of artists and engravers to depict the flora and fauna of the new continents she was conquering. A few examples of their work have been included in this book (Daniel's 'Scorpion' and 'Lions attacking a giraffe').

The telephoto lense on the camera has replaced the telescopic sight on the rifle. As trophy, the fine photograph or movie is frequently preferred to the stuffed and mounted head. Nevertheless, the practical need to cull animals can still provide the hunter with the luxury of killing; and, of course, there are game farms, which strike us as no more or less immoral than farming cattle for the abattoir: particularly as such farms may save species from extermination.

Man has a lot to answer for. This one clever, omnivorous ape (or Yahoo as Swift called him in *Gulliver's Travels*) has run wild and become a threat

to every other form of life. He has already killed off certain species (see 'The Quagga – a Learned Obituary'). There is reason to doubt whether he will even spare himself. He has virtually wiped out all the hunter-gatherers who refused to be 'civilised'. His capacity to reproduce his kind indiscriminately is matched only by his heartless expertise in mass slaughterings of his own species.

Yet this creature is capable of some insight, moments of reflection, reason, justice, mercy. He is extraordinarily clever and inventive. Whereas most other creatures are what they are because they have adapted themselves to particular environments, man has learnt how to adapt wide range of environments to himself: so successfully that he has set up a complex unnatural parasitic system which (as far as the rest of life on earth is concerned) can best be described as a rapidly proliferating cancer, with secondaries everywhere.

Still part of the animal world, Man is aware in a way that animals are not. He is aware of time and of death.

> Nor dread nor hope attend
> A dying animal;
> A man awaits his end
> Dreading and hoping all
>   (W.B. Yeats, 'Death')

Many of man's distinguishing characteristics spring from this awareness, and much of his philosophy and religion are concerned with death, and possible lives after death. He is also a great builder of realities which are subject to death — buildings, works of art, writings, records which create worlds of thought and feeling in colour and music which can continue almost regardles of the lives and deaths of those who transmit them. In those great streams of tradition and cultural history, oral or written, our friends the animals live with us, but in many different shapes and roles depending on our need for them at the time. A poem — or a picture — of an animal is always about the animal *and* something else: and that something else is part of man:

> We carry within us the wonder we seek without us.
> There is all Africa and her prodigies in us,

said Sir Thomas Browne (*Religio Medici* 1643). The splendid frescoes of bird and animal life in the long corridors of the Egyptian Tombs are not there for decoration only; nor are the paintings in thousands of caves, large and small, throughout Southern Africa. They are acts of magic, of communion, of worship, evidence of a more than secular awareness of the beasts they depict and sometimes defy.

We must expect, then, a very wide range of poetic response to the animals which God created before He put them all at risk by creating one in His own image, man.

Animal Poetry

Until the early nineteenth century poems about wild animals are rare in European poetry. As always, there are exceptions. That medieval masterpiece, *Sir Gawain and the Green Knight*, contains three hunts, of a stag, a boar, and a fox — each portrayed with fine realism and profound symbolic overtones; and Shakespeare (*Venus and Adonis* 673-708) in an extended simile gives a moving account of a hare in flight from the hounds. When the wild animal poem does arrive, it does so with a bang, with Blake's hypnotic lyric ' The Tyger', burning in terrible splendour in the forests of the night. Blake also gives us a companion piece, 'The Lamb', the innocent, devoted victim. This immemorial opposition between gentle herbivore and ruthless carnivore appears frequently enough with resonant religious and cosmic overtones, in the poems that follow, (e.g. Bruce Hewett, 'The Leopard').

In European literature the animal poem seems to accompany the growing awareness of nature in other newly discovered continents. Linnaeus and Darwin are the patron saints of the genre; their favourite hunter is hunting not for quarry, but for a specimen to describe, classify and illustrate. Even the traditional sportsman-hunter brings a growing sensibility to the hunt. Cornwallis Harris lards his adventures with quotations from the poets, and uses all his verbal gifts and skills with pen and brush to do justice to the beauty of his victims. In Hjalmar Thesen's 'Koodoo' the same ambivalence is expressed — a poem which makes a nice contrast with Livingstone's 'Clouds' where the hunter does not pull the trigger.

Most of our poems focus on a single beast. We felt, however, that it would be untrue to nature merely to present a portrait gallery of individual animals. Animals appear in particular habitats and frequently in typical chosen company; most animal lovers are sensitive to their complex community life with other animals — and of weather, landscape, vegetation. So we have provided an opening section of general poems which alert us to the landscape.

As so often in South African poetry the best starting point is Thomas Pringle. 'Afar in the Desert' devotes two of its five sections to the human discontents and griefs which have persuaded the speaker to turn his back on mankind and to seek consolation in nature. At first we are in a well-watered world, the lower reaches perhaps of the Winterberg and Amatolas which the poet knew well — 'the skirts of grey forests'; pools and marshy ground, with characteristic creatures, the elephant, the hippo, the buffalo. No creature here seems to be in a hurry; the oribi 'plays', while the elephant 'browses' peacefully, the ungainly hippo 'gambols', the rhino 'wallows' and the zebra drinks undisturbed.

In the next section we cross the dry plains of the brown Karoo, where the plaintive sounds of a springbok's fawn and quagga's neigh help to create a tense scene through which beasts, like the zebra and antelope, fly from their pursuers.

The final section takes us to the desert proper, seldom visited even by hunting tribesmen, 'which the snake and the lizard inhabit alone', and where the desert vegetation is spiny or poisonous. This almost waterless, lifeless zone is the true desert, in which man might feel close to God.

Not many go on such a pilgrimage. Safaris into the deserts are much rarer than visits to game parks, where visitors are reasonably confident that they will encounter a variety of fauna. Their characteristic destination is a waterhole toward sundown when the animals come to drink (see Roy Keech: 'Msinga Five Thirty'). Unlike Pringle's pilgrim, they come without the 'death-fraught firelock' in their hands: they are armed with a camera only; whose little click, however, is enough to alert the wide range of creatures enjoying their sundowner. Here the motive is not escape from man or civilisation: it is sheer enjoyment: 'Let's hang on and watch a bit' — watch the incredible variety of the creatures and their individual movements and stances — wildebeeste, zebra, ibis, warthog.

In Livingstone's 'Bamboo Day' there is no pilgrim is search of God, no conservationist, no nature lover taking photographs of game. Man does not figure at all. The observing eye is impersonal. The description of the natural scene is accurate and objective: the life-giving sun is paradoxically the ally of the common enemy, drought. Vegetation is parched, the herbivores are starving. The carnivores, however, are not hungry, nor are the decomposers, the vultures and jackals: for them there is ample food. The dependence of the whole interlocking system — from elephant grass to lion — on the delayed rains is apparent in the arid air of expectancy. The heralding of the thunderstorm and its enormous approach is accurately and impressively evoked. Few poems depict so well the apparent indifference of nature to the life which she nurtures.

39

Nature in Africa is not to be confused with the benign nature of Wordsworth. There are no crocodiles or hippos in the Lake District, and the wildest beast in Britain is a badger or a fox. Wordsworth's nature has been partially domesticated. In his England no hunter-gatherers survive, and very few pastoralists. Almost every acre is hand tended. The agricultural revolution is complete. By contrast, Africa's climate is intemperate, and her weather is unpredictable; and the sheer scale is greater. This continental contrast is clear if we glance at our rivers.

Few of the rivers of Southern Africa are navigable. Many are sandy chasms for months at a stretch. Suddenly, with the great rains, they become brown torrents bursting their banks. Indeed, the river in flood becomes, for Plomer, a symbol of the impersonal violence of Africa for which European poetry has not prepared him.

'The Scorpion' starts:

Limpopo and Tugela churned
In flood for brown and angry miles,
Melons, maize, domestic thatch,
The trunks of trees, and crocodiles.

This periodic reduction of all forms of life to flotsam on a mighty river is used by Ruth Miller ('The Floating Island') to suggest the certain doom that awaits us all.

But in 'Animal Kingdom' Clouts uses the river in a gentler mood as an image of the mysterious individual life of the creatures who inhabit it or drink from it, each reflecting the sun's light in its own way. Who can define what is happening when the sun shines on the contented creatures? The poet suggests that the purpose of life ('the senior core of the sun') is to make hungry ('I want'), to gratify ('I have'), to satisfy others ('I give'), to respond in mutuality ('I love'). Now, fulfilment lies in a conscious acknowledgement of, and rejoicing in, this living process: he not only praises and articulates the life of the creatures; the creatures enable him to extend his modes of being:

Locust locust leap with me
Water flow and mirror me.

Notes and Acknowledgements

Pictures

Each animal has at least one black-and-white ikon devoted to him, a picture which captures something of his essence, his inscape.

Thirty-two of these are by the greatest animal painters of all time; the Bushmen; two African wood carvings, two African linocuts. These copies were made by Lindy Huggins (24), and Sue Ross (8).

There are five nineteenth century engravings. There is a fine etching by H.A. Aschenborn, and a superb painting by Fritz Krampe. We are happy to include a drawing of giraffes by Roy Campbell, and wish to thank the Niven Trust for Caldwell's 'Monkey'.

Thirteen of the illustrations have been drawn specially for this work - by Cecil Skotnes (three), Claire Gavronsky (two), Leigh Voigt (two) and Lindy Huggins (six).

The cover illustration has been specially painted by Gordon Vorster for this book.

Among the many who contributed suggestions and ideas are Professors Robert Brooks, Alan Crump, Herbert Pahl, E.J. de Jager, Dr Peter Alexander, Emily O'Meara, Lois Gardner, Estelle Marais, Wilma Stockenström and Douglas Livingstone.

Zoological Notes

Carmen Welz's notes frequently provide information chosen for its relevance to aspects of poems which otherwise might remain obscure.

The Poems

We have chosen forty-five animals for our ark. Some of them have only one poem devoted to them, others have as many as eight. We have included seven poems which concentrate on the animals in their setting, and 123 on individual animals or small groups.

Of the forty-nine poets, thirty-one are South Africans or Zimbabweans who use English for preference; seven are Afrikaans, whose poems have been translated; three are from West Africa, one from Kenya; and ten are British or American. (It is noticeable that metropolitan writers adopt a humorous stance towards the animals of Africa. Hilaire Belloc and Ogden Nash are responsible for most of our laughs.)

Our selection seems to show that South Africa has produced a clutch of powerful but very different practitioners in the field. Without the contributions of Livingstone (ten), Hewett (seven), Clouts (six), Malony (six), Brettell (four) and Fairbridge (four) the book would hardly exist and without Woodhouse's and Markowitz's English renderings of Bushmen stories it would have lacked an important element. Our debt to translators, and particularly George Fortune, is great.

Proverbs and Folktales

Until the wholesale disturbance of the ecology which has followed white settlement, man and animals lived in familiar contact. African cultures abound in proverbs drawn from observation of animals, and in myths with religious and cosmological significances. Wherever possible we have found one or more proverbs for each animal – from Zulu, Xhosa, Sechuana and Shona. Our choice was limited by the shortage of reference works in this field. Two works call for particular praise: Solomon Plaatje's *Sechuana Proverbs*, in which he frequently finds a European equivalent, and Lincoln Nyembesi's *Zulu Proverbs*. In twelve cases we resorted to Bushman Myths, taken in the main from Bert Woodhouse's *When Animals were People*, a title which indicates the intimacy of man and animal in that society: a vein which has been explored repeatedly by Laurens van der Post, Arthur Markowitz and other writers on the Bushman.

Libraries
Our greatest debt is to the National English Literary Museum, Grahamstown, for help with biographical and bibliographical material; to the British Library, London; the Cory Library for Historical Research, Rhodes University, Grahamstown; The Gubbins Collection, University of the Witwatersrand; The Johannesburg Art Gallery; The Johannesburg Public Library; The Pretoria Art Gallery; The South African Library, Cape Town.

We are grateful for assistance and encouragement received from the Department of Nature and Environmental Conservation, Cape Town; The National Parks Board, Pretoria; SATOUR, Pretoria; and the South African Wild Life Society.

Our thanks are also due to Maureen Pyott, for checking the draft; and to Pat Papenfus for much labour and patience with the typescript over a long period.

Animals in the Landscape

from THE FLAMING TERRAPIN

Out of the Ark's grim hold
A torrent of spendour rolled -
From the hollow resounding sides,
Flashing and glittering, came
Panthers with sparkled hides,
And tigers scribbled with flame,
And lions in grisly trains
Cascading their golden manes.
They ramped in the morning light,
And over their stripes and stars
The sun-shot lightnings, quivering bright,
Rippled in zigzag bars.
The wildebeest frisked with the gale
On the crags of a hunchback mountain,
With his heels in the clouds, he flirted his tail
Like the jet of a silvery fountain.
Frail oribi sailed with their golden-skinned
And feathery limbs laid light on the wind.
And the springbok bounced, and fluttered, and flew,
Hooping their spines on the gaunt karroo.
Grey zebras pranced and snorted aloud —
With the crackle of hail their hard hoofs pelt,
And thunder breaks from the rolling cloud
That they raise on the dusty Veldt.
O, hark how the rapids of the Congo
Are chanting their rolling strains,
And the sun-dappled herds a-skipping to the song, go
Kicking up the dust on the great, grey plains -
Tsessebe, Koodoo, Buffalo, Bongo,
With the fierce wind foaming in their manes.

Roy Campbell

AFAR IN THE DESERT

Afar in the desert I love to ride,
With the silent Bush-boy alone by my side:
When the sorrows of life the soul o'ercast,
And, sick of the Present, I cling to the Past;
When the eye is suffused with regretful tears,
From the fond recollections of former years;
And shadows of things that have long since fled
Flit over the brain, like the ghosts of the dead:
Bright visions of glory — that vanished too soon;
Day dreams — that departed ere manhood's noon;
Attachments — by fate or by falsehood reft;
Companions of early days — lost or left;
And my native Land — whose magical name
Thrills to the heart like electric flames;
The home of my childhood; the haunts of my prime;
All the passions and scenes of that rapturous time
When the feelings were young and the world was new,
Like the fresh flowers of Eden unfolding to view;
All — all now forsaken — forgotten — foregone!
And I — a lone exile remembered by none —
My high aims abandoned, — my good acts undone, —
Aweary of all that is under the sun, —
With the sadness of heart which no stranger may scan,
I fly to the desert, afar from man!

Afar in the desert I love to ride,
With the silent Bush-boy alone by my side:
When the wild turmoil of this wearisome life,
With its scenes of oppression, corruption, and strife —
The proud man's frown, and the base man's fear, —
The scorner's laugh, and the sufferer's tear, —
And malice, and meanness, and falsehood, and folly,
Dispose me to musing and dark melancholy;
When my bosom is full, and my thoughts are high,
And my soul is sick with the bondsman's sigh —
Oh! then there is freedom, and joy, and pride,
Afar in the desert alone to ride!

There is rapture to vault on the champing steed,
And to bound away with the eagle's speed,
With the death-fraught firelock in my hand —
The only law in the Desert Land!

Afar in the desert I love to ride,
With the silent Bush-boy alone by my side:
Away, away, from the dwellings of men,
By the wild deer's haunt, by the buffalo's glen;
By valleys remote where the oribi plays,
Where the gnu, the gazelle, and the hartebeest graze,
And the kudu and eland unhunted recline
By the skirts of grey forests o'erhung with wild vine;
Where the elephant browses at peace in his wood,
And the river-horse gambols unscared in the flood,
And the mighty rhinoceros wallows at will
In the fen where the wild ass is drinking his fill.

Afar in the desert I love to ride,
With the silent Bush-boy alone by my side:
O'er the brown Karroo, where the bleating cry
Of the springbok's fawn sounds plaintively;
And the timorous quagga's shrill whistling neigh

Is heard by the fountain at twilight grey;
Where the zebra wantonly tosses his mane,
With wild hoof scouring the desolate plain;
And the fleet-footed ostrich over the waste
Speeds like a horseman who travels in haste,
Hieing away to the home of her rest
Where she and her mate have scooped their nest,
Far hid from the pitiless plunderer's view
In the pathless depths of the parched Karroo.

Afar in the desert I love to ride,
With the silent Bush-boy alone by my side:
Away, away, in the wilderness vast,
Where the white man's foot hath never passed,
And the quivered Coranna or Bechuan
Hath rarely crossed with his roving clan:
A region of emptiness, howling and drear,
Which man hath abandoned from famine and fear
Which the snake and the lizard inhabit alone,
With the twilight bat from the yawning stone;
Where grass, nor herb, nor shrub takes root,
Save poisonous thorns that pierce the foot;
And the bitter-melon, for food and drink,
Is the pilgrim's fare by the salt lake's brink:
A region of drought, where no river glides,
Nor rippling brook with osiered sides;
Where sedgy pool, nor bubbling fount,
Nor tree, nor cloud, nor misty mount,
Appears, to refresh the aching eye:
But the barren earth, and the burning sky,
And the blank horizon, round and round,
Spread - void of living sight and sound;
And here, while the night-winds round me sigh,
And the stars burn bright in the midnight sky.
As I sit apart by the desert stone,
Like Elijah at Horeb's cave alone,
'A still small voice' comes through the wild
(Like a father consoling his fretful child),
Which banishes bitterness, wrath, and fear, —
Saying — MAN IS DISTANT, BUT GOD IS NEAR!

Thomas Pringle

SILENCE ALLOWED
Msinga Mkusi Five-Thirty

Nine wildebeests sip the sedged water of the pool.
You can count them man as well as I
And nick them on your hidden spool. Nine
Jostled minds combined behind
Hat-rack buffalo horns — but your click
Has set the ibis on that grey drowned tree
Honking for all its worth and made the flanker
Twitch his mane, snort, become regardant gnu. Away go
Zebra hoofing it on the thorn-track and even the three
Wart-hog, confident as rats they were, stand stock-still
In the pan.
    Only the coots go plashing on at lily play.
Look, keep that flipping shutter shut, and there's a chance that
That wart-hog sow will, dipping her dali tusks,
Daintily bring her snout down to the green quench again
And the hadedah's bill will backprod for lice
Nibbling and ruffling in its wing-feathers,
And all that brindle Catalan beef
Of the wildebeests will sip again; some of it
Butting foreheads in the moistened sand
Until its own moose-like restlessness
Perturbs all nine — then hell what a crash canter
Distal tufts awave out into the thorny plain of day.
Let's hang on and watch the coots a bit. Silence
Summoned, who knows, zebra may come zigzagging back.

Roy Keech

A BAMBOO DAY

To step from squat foothills across
the early-morning, already crackling plain
    to the thin green gully that pipes
a river, drowned in dust, seawards, is but
    one stride of a raincloud's seven-league boots;
but there has been no rain for eighteen months.

The gully cups a mud-stained palm
of water: the mayhem on the plain makes way
    for the green strip. A solitary
rakeribbed lion lies lolling his tongue for coolness
    near pyjama-ed zebra and lumpy
wildebeest disgustedly pawing at thorns.

Slim brown-eyed buck stand balancing
their too heavy horns and sprung hindquarters
    delicately on the fulcrum
of their forward hooves, giraffe, their heads swimming,
    stand tall to eat the shade or watch,
blinking, for the outflanking, knife-toed leopards.

The cats, no respecters of truces,
who cut and thrust about the trampled pool
    using drought the common enemy
as a time for killing and killing like
    any other, are holed up somewhere
digesting, leaving shattered carcasses.

A clump of giant bamboos stands still
some yards back from the water as if waiting
    on winds to cool its dusty columns.
Elephant grass bends, khaki, itchy, separate,
    as if the blades cannot bear to touch.
Insensate, the heat stamps raging on the world.

The sun boils blindly at its task
of treading plasma from eyeballs and blood,
    shrivelling heart sinews, squeezing salt.
A quick shriek of vultures squabbling with jackals
    over meat, dies; there is enough.
Life, under brass, bakes through the torpid day.

Lifting and twirling the soft capes
of dustdevils in its wake, a breeze arrives.
Every head alerts unblinking
as one of the bamboos bursts like a gunshot,
perhaps with uncontainable joy.
Over the far foothills, a shadow forms.

Swelling, shaped into a massive
cerebellum, sharply veined by intermittent
lightning jags, the unheard thunder
tumbling small eddies of dead leaves towards itself,
the cloud balloons. A world holds still.
Winds start to caper gravely in the trees.

The distant yellow of the plain
blackens and starts to roll towards the standing herds.
It will be half-an-hour yet before
the rain comes to smash down its silver gifts
and swell the mud choked gully's throat,
but the lion has stretched to find himself alone.

Douglas Livingstone

THE FLOATING ISLAND

Down the glutted river's throat
Jut the jagged trunks of trees,
Giddily the bubbles float;
The dead drowned buck have wounded knees.
The basket nests ooze mud in sodden trees.

Swirling in a giddy gyre
Down the brown Zambesi floor
Comes an island — torn entire
With tendon reeds and brackish blood,
Prised from its moorings in the silent mud,

Bearing on its swinging arc
A herd of buck, alive, aground,
With anguished eyes, their wet flanks dark
With sweat. The water gabbles round.
Their sucking hoofprints moon the mud with sound.

The sliding scenery repeats
The gliding greenery of fear.
A newborn buck gropes for the teats;
Green to terror, he does not hear
The lipping tongues around his mother's feet.

Head back flat, with seashell horn
Against the wind the leader strains.
Around him lean the does and fawns:
They can remember summer rains —
But not like these. Not these obliterated plains.

Do they smell the tumbling doom
Scarved in silken spray that slides
To the falling ledge, that looms
But one nightfall on? Their sides
Bulge and flatten. Their eyes darken and grow wide.

Along the gorged Zambesi swims
In a slow insensate dance
Frieze of buck with dervish limbs
Frozen in a dreamer's trance.
Anarchy has leapt beyond mischance.

A nightfall on the Smoke that Thunders[1]
Will spring to gulf their leaping sides.
Wrenched from our continent, we blunder
And lacking weather-sense for guide
Our green uncharted islands sink in ravelled floods, blind-eyed.

Ruth Miller

[1]*The Smoke That Thunders:* African name for the Victoria Falls.

ANIMAL KINGDOM

Spading earth
I thought of the earth. Here
and there gazelle and hog
locust and elephant
fly and frog,
collecting their light, leapt
frumped pondered and whizzed
and the river that I heard
included birdsong.

What happens when the sun
dewed with such joy, shines on, spills down
on gazelle and hog
locust and elephant
fly and frog
pond hand stalk and loquat
river and beak?

I want I have I give I love
I answer the senior core of the sun
I speed the body of the warm gazelle
I lift the elephant high in my thought
like a cloud of heaven that moves so slow,
and the fly I follow, the dustheap find
my plumtree grows from a clod of sleep.
Locust locust leap with me
water flow and mirror me.

Sydney Clouts

FROM A VOYAGE TO AFRICA PART III

How gentle, courteous, and noble is nature
Whose beasts, when visible, appear dumb and good,
And whose prospects, munificent but pure;
Or she is cruel if that should be the mood,
May be dressed in or divested of allure.

A mirror more perfect than any of glass
She is: when looked in, the looker sees a shape
Of his emotion, and of what really was
There, looking in; of an angel or an ape.
If her mountains lelan toward beguiling us -

In whom, once, we saw a visage of our fright,
Though long ago, and in another country,
Whereas today they flatter us with their height -
O nature, mirror or mishandled pantry,
Or medicine, goddess, enemy, what you like -

I love you, and knowing whom I really love,
I find it difficult not to love you more;
Either in a city's confines, at one remove,
Or when I, travelling past in train or car,
Touch the innocence your wildernesses prove.

David Wright

ANT Genus *Formicidae;* Order *Hymenoptera* - which includes bees, wasps, etc.

NAMES
English: *Ants - red, sugar, Argentinian, etc. Although termites are*
             popularly known as white ants, they belong to an entirely
             different insect order.
Afrikaans: *Miere - rooimiere, ens.*
African: *(Z) intuthwane (black), itsheketshe (red) (N-S) tshosane (red)*

DISTRIBUTION: Worldwide

DIET: Varied. Some are carnivorous, others live on honeydew and nectar, some feed mainly on grass seeds and still others are domestic, swarming over such foodstuffs as cakes, sweets and leftovers.

FEATURES AND HABITS: There are some 10 000 species of ants in the world and about 400 varieties and species in Africa, south of the Zambezi River. They vary greatly in size, appearance and habit. They are social insects and live in colonies, small or large. There are no known solitary ants. All ants go through four stages; egg, larva, pupa and adult. Generally a colony is made up of one or more queens and a multitude of sterile females who perform various duties. Males are encountered only at certain times, (and never as 'kings' as is the case with termites). They are variously equipped with stings, powerful jaws or glands which produce an offensive fluid or the poison, formic acid.

THE ANT

The ant has made himself illustrious
Through constant industry industrious.
So what?
Would you be calm and placid
If you were full of formic acid?

Ogden Nash

EXTRACT FROM CANTO LXXXI

The ant's a centaur in his dragon world
Pull down thy vanity, it is not man
Made courage, or made order, or made grace,
    Pull down thy vanity, I say pull down.
Learn of the green world what can be thy place
In scaled invention or true artistry,
Pull down thy vanity,
                Paquin pull down!
The green casque has outdone your elegance.
'Master thyself, then others shall thee beare.'

Ezra Pound

BY AN ANT-HEAP

Within this termitary
is no dormitory.
   Sexless and blind,
the workers bustle
along the tunnels
   with soldier guides.

There is no frillery
in any gallery:
all is for use,
thrown-up food,
carcases, excrement
(eaten for increment,
then used for building).
All is utility:
the fattened queen's
an egg-machine.

              The king alone,
                  small as a commoner
       beneath her corpulence,
       sits in indolence
            and is forgotten.
       Yet it is he
       who gives the seed —
       who has been the father
       of more than half.

What does it matter?
       when they are old
           (the royal couple),
when the queen miscarries
       or eggs come slow,
           no one will trouble
to bring them food:
all is for use
and themselves are food.

Terence Heywood

TO YOU, ANT

Ant, who gave you your unique skill
To pile up soil in that weird conical mount at your doorstep
So that when it rains the water will be run off without
    getting into your house?
Ant, my friend, you are a genius.

I envy your strength, Ant.
Bees and crickets are no match for you in a fight;
And with a long stick you even strike away at scorpions,
You have never been beaten in a fight.

Ant, where from do you get your daring?
You enter an elephant's trunk and it throws itself about in pain;
You attack and smother to death a giant python;
And you can even crawl on the chin of a sleeping crocodile.

Where from does your strength come, Ant?
You dig a hole that never bends;
You hollow your way through the trunks of trees
Digging deeper passing on down beyond the roots.

Ant, you are the pillar of your house.
At the birth of your child
You go to hunt for food in deep dark forests,
Ant, your ways will never cease to surprise me.

Ant, you are indeed a great hunter;
You never fail to give your children food;
You care for the nursing mothers with loving gentleness.
No one ever goes hungry in your household.

Tell me Ant, where did you get this love?
There is no jealousy nor stinting in your city.
You work all day long without complaining or grumbling.
Please lend me your heart for just one day.

Ant, why is it that you never seem to grow old?
Unless someone steps on you and kills you, I haven't seen your
    corpse anywhere.
Please give me your knowledge of life
So that I can help my children and friends.

Translated from the original Shona by the Literature Bureau

A.G. Mandishona

TO COME BACK HOME

To come back home
        And find your pillow
            An ant-hill of ants
                That gnawed your
                    father
                    mother
                    brother
                    sister
Exhumes the agony
That sent you away
With a knotted promise
To come back home.

S Chimsoro

Uzingikel' ubu-xwangu.
He is turning up for himself a mass of red ants.

A person by some expression or statement better left unsaid has
brought upon himself virulent antagonism and biting criticism.

Xhosa

ANTBEAR *Orycteropus afer*

NAMES
English: *antbear, aardvark*
Afrikaans: *erdvark, miervreter*
African: *isambane (Z), thakadu (N-S)*

59

DISTRIBUTION: Throughout Africa, but sporadic. Not in very dry areas such as the Namib.

DIET: Primarily termites but also ants and sometimes soft fruits.

FEATURES AND HABITS: Fossorial by day and therefore seldom seen. A solitary animal, except when mating or with young. With its powerful claws it digs open termite mounds and then probes around in the passages for its prey with a viscid, worm-like tongue. Has no real teeth. The female has a burrow system of many chambers and entrances which is used as a permanent shelter, and may extend deep underground. When in danger it can dig at such a rate as to vanish from sight within a few minutes. It is preyed upon by larger predators and its meat is regarded as a delicacy by some people. Breeding season is probably early summer and a single young is born. A soft snuffling is the only sound it makes. A useful animal, especially where termites are a problem.

ANTBEAR

Filching an odd half-hour of winter light
The queer clown of a beast strolled on my afternoon.
You ancient tenant of my red soil under —
Am I your guest, or are you mine, I wonder?
I am your debtor, that is certain, with your boon
Of licking appetite.
Mousing and miching, snuffle and flurry of dust,
Busy, but not over-busy, ambling and shambling,
Content to satisfy your yokel's lust
On earthy foraging.
Small brainbox, slender snout, powerful behind,
Dim eyes to blink only at the lonely stars,
No teeth to nip, only to squash and grind,
And claws only for Adam's task, not Mars'.
Innocent, with no guile,
Like all surly wits, hermits, world-forsakers,
Surviving, they say, only in our warm acres,
To make my day worthwhile.

He scents my nearness with a sudden start —
Snuff of the quivering snout
Flap of the batlike ears.

Yes, shuffle off. The farewell of the winter sun
Throws its wan aureole not on your head but on your bum:
That's where your treasure is.
In gross ungracious haste, yes, take your flight,
In cavernous setts delved down to the rocks
Squirm through the labyrinth of your dusty den:

But keep the man far hence that's kin to fox,
For with his lust, he'll dig you up again.

N.H. Brettell

Ubekwe yisambane.
He has been looked at by the antbear.

The antbear moves about with eyes cast down as if shy. When,
therefore, it raises its eyes to look at a person, that is
regarded as an ill-omen.

The saying means that one has been unfortunate in a quest.

Zulu

BABOON More than a dozen species of African monkeys which have become ground-dwellers. *Papio ursinus* or chacma is the commonest species in Southern Africa.

NAMES
English: *Chacma baboon, Cape baboon*
Afrikaans: *Gewone bobbejaan, Kaapse bobbejaan*
African: *imfene (Z), tshwene (N-S), bvene (Sh)*

DISTRIBUTION: From the Cape Peninsula northwards to the southern parts of Angola, Zimbabwe and Mozambique. It inhabits mountains and hilly country but must be near water.

DIET: Omnivorous; e.g. bulbs, fruit, mealies, insects and eggs.

FEATURES AND HABITS: Gregarious, diurnal animals. Troops range in size between ten and one hundred animals, dominated by a number of full-grown males. There is no foundation for the old belief that they put out sentries while feeding. The leopard is their chief enemy, but they are also killed by man because they cause crop damage. There is no fixed mating season. A single young is born after a gestation of six months. They may live to 45 years.

THE THEOLOGY OF BONGWI, THE BABOON

This is the wisdom of the Ape
  Who yelps beneath the Moon
'Tis God who made me in His shape
  He is a great Baboon.
'Tis He who tilts the moon askew
  And fans the forest trees,
The heavens which are broad and blue
  Provide him his trapeze;
He swings with tail divinely bent
  Around those azure bars
And munches to his Soul's content
  The kernels of the stars;
And when I die, His loving care
  Will raise me from the sod
To learn the perfect Mischief there,
  The Nimbleness of God.

Roy Campbell

THE PRAISES OF BABOON, THE TOTEM ANIMAL

(as recorded by Aaron C. Hodza)

Masters of the forests.
Those who make the rain to fall.
And who make all kinds of caterpillars come.
Sons of the Leader of big groups.
Their young clinging on to their backs.
Those of the long faces.
Smooth as a log without any bark.
Watchmen.
Those of the gruff voices.
Swaying to and fro in the trees.
Swarming here and there in the fields.
In the rains and just before always searching for food.
Animal almost human.
Knowing where the wild plums and the wild loquats are.

'I climb Rupara with my teeth;
And on the summit I cry defiance.
But among ants I hold Tom Thumb with my foot.'

Fellows with unkempt hair,
Their body knows water only when it rains.
One who takes everything,
Even the wild bulbs and wild onions here.

'I forage all over, a bull of Tingini.
Walking as if I do not see,
But I see very well indeed.
Among scorpions as well, I hold Tom Thumb in my foot.
Walking, you would say I was planting ground-peas,
And running, you'd think I was planting ground-nuts.'

Translated from the Shona by George Fortune

BONGWI

A haunted soul put under ban,
    A hunted beast that has to roam
The voiceless image of a man
    With neither speech nor home -

Upon the summit of the height,
    Where only wind-swept lichens grow,
Bongwi, lit by the dawning-light,
    Watches the plain below.

Fierce eyes, low brow, protruding mouth,
    Short hands that twitch and twitch again,
The hairy gargoyle of the South -
    A man without a brain;

Upon the highest krantz he waits
    Dim-lit by golden streak of dawn,
Guarding the interests of his mates
    Who wreck the fields of corn.

Far down the mealie-gardens lie,
    And he a patient sentinel,
Shouts 'Boor-hoom!' to the offended sky
    To show that all is well.

A white fish-eagle sails along,
    His mighty pinions harping tunes
Till dawn throbs with Aeolian song
    And, far below, the brown baboons

Look up and note the paling East,
    The fading moon, the stars that wane,
And, gorg'd, they quit their stolen feast
    And seek the open veld again.

And Bongwi sees. But turns his view -
    Brown-eyed — towards the breaking morn,
And gazes through the soundless blue
    The golden distance of the dawn.

Kingsley Fairbridge

Zvine manenji kuti gudo ripunzike mumuti.

It is remarkable that the baboon should fall from a tree.

i.e. that experts should fail.

Shona

Bvene kiupa kiupa zvaro asi haridyi chakafa choga.

The baboon is indeed ugly, but it does not eat dead things.

i.e. Even the worst person has his redeeming features.

Shona

BUFFALO *Syncerus caffer*

NAMES
English: *buffalo, Cape - or African buffalo,*
Afrikaans: *buffel, Afrikaanse buffel*
African: *inyathi (Z), nare (N-S)*

DISTRIBUTION: Formerly they ranged across the greater part of Africa south of the Sahara. In South Africa today, they are found only in the Kruger National Park, and in small herds in the Eastern Cape and Zululand.

DIET: They are mainly grazers but do some browsing.

FEATURES AND HABITS: A gregarious animal, usually found in large herds, but smaller herds and solitary bulls also common. Normally they feed in the later afternoon, at night and early in the morning. The hot hours of the day are spent in the shade of dense bush. Buffalo enjoy wallowing in muddy pools to keep cool; the mud affords some protection against parasites. Oxpeckers are constant companions and help rid them of ticks and stinging flies. They are not unduly aggressive except when under attack. Because they are intelligent and cunning, they rank amongst the most dangerous game when wounded. Even lions, only significant natural enemy, prefer to catch cows, calves or solitary old bulls. They tend to stampede when alarmed. Towards the end of the nineteenth century they were very nearly exterminated by the rinderpest, but they are the second most numerous species in the Kruger Park today. Calves are normally born during summer after a gestation of eleven months.

BUFFALO

In kraals of slanting shade the herd
Moves restively; flared nostrils vent
The cordite fumes of summer, snuff
The dung of slow diminishment.
Old sagas of migration vex
Their torpor with blood memories
Of boundless grazing, pools and hides,
Fights and strong seasonal increase.

Curved boss thrust down, imperial
In hump of shoulder, loop of horn,
A great bull hoofs the dust; his squat
Flanks twitch and rope with muscles worn
By treks and mating: master still
Of cows he sired or won, and hot
Young bulls, his signal temper draws
The phalanx round him in a knot.

Slow, tentative, the sickled heads
Are lifted; incandescent eyes
Reflect, beyond their range of sight,
The swelling thunder buds that rise
In soundless tumult to discharge
The storm; no fear or challenge cracks
Its whip-lash: dull, incurious,
They drop their heads and hunch their backs.

And by their sloth the old bull knows
His impotence: the lowing sky
Commands more sweetly, the breathing rain,
Than he can warm. In mute reply,
He stands defiantly to meet
The sleek new leader of the herd -
The Bull of Heaven charging down
To graze the pastures, tame and lourd.

                                        Charles Eglington

THE BUFFALO

Encased in mud, and breathing valley steam,
And teased all day by clouds of stinging flies,
That smother round his flanks and mouth and eyes,
Provoking rage, till an unlidded gleam
Darts from each eye across the sombre stream,
And his great bulk is shaken, to surprise
And scare away the pestering hosts, that rise
Black in the air about him; parrots scream
Above him in the tangled overgrowth,
And monkeys chatter, and the green snake glides
From branch to branch with supple weaving thews;
But he, though irked by noise and stir, is loth
To leave the wallowing-pool that coats his sides
And back and belly with protective ooze.

                                        Herbert Price

69

LONE BULL

The bush is quiet and heavy with heat,
crackling with the noises of the afternoon.

The wind rises and falls amongst the mountains,
herded by sun and stone like a flight
of leisure birds flocked by poised hawks.

More tangible herds below move at a crawl —
or don't move at all — the solitary strays
bask in the closeness of comfort and call.

But there is too much of the sun pouring
its heat into the long grass,
where a sudden electric twig snaps to flame.

The lone bull on the ground's far swell
is the first drugged by the brutal air
that rolls like thunder from the South.

One by one the animals stiffen, moments
only before the scattering frenzy clears blood,
and flame echoes in a smothering rumble

of hooves. Dust hides the wind's betrayal;
dust hides the flight, and darkness coming,
over the sight of a single shape, dimming

into sound ...

In depths of the far-hidden conical funnels
of the crags he stands alone, soundless
in the heavy updraft of air that soothes

the agony of his bowed head like smoke
into a patch of high sky above the burning
ropes of darkness and pain with which he's bound.

Charl J.F. Cilliers

Ihlatshw' ifaluthele.

The buffalo is slaughtered from the back.

The buffalo's horns are its most dangerous part. To kill it, therefore, it is safer to approach it from behind and take it unawares.

This is said when a person is treated in a treacherous manner in his absence.

Zulu

Ungibophel' amanqin' enyathi.

He has tied for me the limbs of a buffalo.

Though a buffalo's limbs may be tied, if its horns are free, it will still be dangerous.

This is said when a person deceives another into believing that a situation is safe when it is not.

Zulu

Iphisi lenyathi lidliwa yinyathi.

The great buffalo hunter is killed by the buffalo.

A person dies in his own trade.

Zulu

CHAMELEON Class *Reptilia* Order *Squamata* Sub-order *Sauria*

NAMES
English: *chameleon*
Afrikaans: *verkleurmannetjie, trapsuutjies*
African: *u(lu)nwabu (Z), leobu (N-S)*

DISTRIBUTION: More than eighty species, most of which are found in Africa and Madagascar. There are some in Spain, Asia Minor, Arabia, Sri Lanka and India.

DIET: Mainly insectivorous.

FEATURES AND HABITS: They are all members of a group of slow moving and deliberate, arboreal lizards. They have the ability to change colour and so blend in with their environment. They capture their prey with club-tipped sticky tongues which can be shot out to a considerable distance. They have extremely mobile eyes which can move independently. Their fingers and toes are arranged in pincer-like bundles. A prehensile tail acts as a stabilising aid when climbing. Some produce live young and others lay eggs. Different species display a wide diversity of appendages such as crests, horns and frills; they vary in length from a few centimetres to more than half a metre. They are quite harmless but when threatened will strike a menacing pose and hiss loudly. For this reason they are greatly feared by many people.

AT A SNAIL'S PACE, PLEASE

At the tip
of a chameleon's tongue
there is a pot of boiling glue
to cook flies for breakfast
before he sets off
on a slow tightwire walk
like a trapeze artist.

Under the belly of every snail
lies a tank full of a low-octane petrol
to propel the minuscule engine
to a destination of a juicy cabbage leaf.

It is overtaken
by American mechanical monsters,
drunk with gallons of gasoline,
that leave highways strewn
with gory confetti of corpses.

The loud Bang!
brings brawny farmers
running from homesteads to render help.

From beehive huts tumble black bumpkins
to gawk at twisted wrecks coated with fresh blood
amid cries of 'Help!'

Ambulances sound shrill sirens,
tearing the silky shawl of the night's silence.
O! speed fiend
whose knell has sounded,
look at the snail
slumbering
in his shell.
See the chameleon
cosy under her quilted coat.

Oswald Mtshali

CHAMELEON

Ancient and leaden-lidded he treads
A branch's tight-rope balancing his double times
Unsteadily, a calculating creeper stirs
Something alive out of extinct tellurian dreams.

Age with blood as green as youth,
Gay as a pigmy sunset painted on a leaf,
A crouching abstract of the sky
And flower and earth, savage in arthritic grief.

Suffers the puppy's caress
Of a bounding wind, unsoftened and not yet undone,
Watching behind his painted walls
In a small darkness, spun on a broken axle of sun,

Juggles the two hemispheres
On the black ridge of our old dilemma, plies
His patient, palaeolithic anger
With a hissing tongue on a diet of present flies.

Anthony Delius

UNDER THE DRIPPING TREES

Under the dripping trees, a small
Wrecked chameleon. The slim mailed keel
Only ever upheld a gargoyle figurehead.
Tilted now, it rests on broken elbows,
Limp pincer-mittens, a glass eye dreaming
Whorls of ants. What caught up with you today?
Always too slow for a marauding cat,
What defence have you but ugliness?
I loved you like no other traveller
In my garden. Often on my arm you poised,
Leaf-light and hesitant, swivelled
A sea-faring eye at me, then, set down
Pressed on into life's tangled stems.
Overcome as you are now with stillness,
Forgive us our haste in your deliberation.
Hard lemon-yellow in the rain: the last
Colour of Joseph's coat. Last of all,
The ants line up to excavate your form,
Carry your meat to the roots.

Rowland Molony

Uqaph' eqolo njengonwabu.
He is watching the back like a chameleon.

The eyes of a chameleon are peculiar in that they are able to turn in all directions, forwards and backwards. The chameleon is, therefore, able to watch happenings in front and behind.

The expression is used of a person who is suspicious, and watches carefully what goes on behind him.

Zulu

Okwakho kunxanye, kufana nesithupha sonwabu.
Yours is peculiar, it is like the thumb of a chameleon.

This is said of a person who does things his own way, a person who cannot be trusted to behave in the generally accepted way. He is likened unto the thumb of a chameleon which is quite peculiar, and not like that of other animals.

Zulu

CHEETAH *Acinonyxa jubatus*

NAMES
English: *cheetah*
Afrikaans: *jagluiperd*
African: *ingulule (Z) ihlosi (N-S)*

DISTRIBUTION: Cheetah still occur widely across Africa and in parts of Asia. In Southern Africa they are today restricted to the less developed northern parts and to certain areas where they have been re-introduced.

DIET: Carnivorous. Prefers smaller herbivores such as impala, duiker or warthogs; larger species may also be taken when several cheetah band together in the hunt. They will also catch animals such as hares and birds.

FEATURES AND HABITS: Slender, hollow-backed animal with a smaller head and longer legs than a leopard. Whereas a leopard's spots are arranged in rosettes, the round and oval spots of the cheetah are distributed evenly. Cheetah move about singly, in pairs, or in small groups. They are largely diurnal, hunting very early in the morning or at twilight. They stalk as close as possible to their quarry and then rush at it with a great burst of speed. They are regarded as the fastest mammals on earth but can only maintain top speed for about half a kilometre. The cheetah has a mild disposition and is some times kept as a pet. Because they are so unagressive they are often robbed of their kill, even by vultures. Litters normally consist of two to four cubs.

CHEETAH

Indolent and kitten-eyed,
This is the bushveld's innocent -
The stealthy leopard parodied
With grinning, gangling pup-content.

Slouching through the tawny grass
Or loose-limbed lolling in the shade,
Purring for the sun to pass
and build a twilight barricade

Around the vast arena where,
In scattered herds, his grazing prey
Do not suspect in what wild fear
They'll join with him in fatal play;

Till hunger draws slack sinews tight
And vibrant as a hunter's bow:
Then, like a fleck of mottled light,
He slides across the still plateau.

A tremor rakes the herds: they scent
The pungent breeze of his advance;
Heads rear and jerk in vigilant
Compliance with the game of chance

In which, of thousands, only one
Is centred in the cheetah's eye;
They wheel and then stampede, for none
Know which it is that has to die.

His stealth and swiftness fling a noose
And as his loping strides begin
To blur with speed, he ropes the loose
Buck on the red horizon in.

Charles Eglington

*Dindingwe rinofara richakweva rimwe asi kuti rave iro rinoti mavara
angu azare vu.*

The cheetah is happy while it drags another but when it is its own
turn, it says, 'My colours are getting soiled.'

i.e. A person complains on being treated as he himself treats others.

Shona

79

COBRA General name given to front-fanged snakes of the genus *Naja*, family *Elapidae*.

NAMES
English: *Yellow or Cape Cobra, Egyptian or Bushveld Cobra, etc.*
Afrikaans:*koperkapel - derived from the Portuguese name 'cobra de capello', i.e. 'serpent of the hood'.*
African: *imfezi, iphimphi (Z)*

DISTRIBUTION: Throughout Africa and southern Asia.

DIET: More or less omnivorous; small rodents, toads, eggs etc. Also cannibalistic.

FEATURES AND HABITS: They rear up and spread a distinct hood when agitated or annoyed. They are all highly poisonous, the venom being neurotoxic. Cobras lay eggs and live in holes in the ground. A great range of colours is found amongst the various species and also within the same species; honey-yellow, olive, browns, slate through to black as well as banded. Because they are alert and intelligent they are used by snake-charmers of the East and North Africa. They do not, as is popularly believed, sway to the music but follow the movement of the flute. Cobras play an important role in religious practices of the ancients.

SALUTE

Very Profound Men have lived in Europe.
On the world's perimeters, sharkfins, anteaters, kangaroo,
    pearloysters, bears,
and others (fit for smiles).

It was the Wolf of Europe that went prowling.

Good morning, gentle cobra, are you well?

Sydney Clouts

ADONIS

Oddly, on this still hot day
noise of wind in the leaves.
I look over the kitchen door, vaguely —
JEEPS! A six-foot cobra on the flagstones!
Leaving me in no doubt he has arrived.

This snake has gone in for body-building,
is all biceps. I peep two eyes over,
staring while he flexes himself in big bends,
I notice he goes in for levering up boulders with his head.
Mr. Universe, six prime frog steaks and a long
draught of dam water every day.

He marches like a river through my flowers,
And pours himself under the rocks.
Aha! I shout (quietly), coming out and
showing myself to the last six inches
of his tail — he doesn't know
I have chest expanders in the bedroom.

Rowland Molony

THE COBRA

The coppery cobra slips out of his hole,
    He sneaks the small hill round:
"The rain has come, the veld is moist
    And moist the red-gold ground."

The meercat comes, he stands erect,
    Watching, with small eyes bright;
The age-old porcupine opines:
    "It will rain again tonight."

But the gekko pipes, "No, it's not rain!
    It's tacky, red and dark.
Who ever saw such rain before,
    So smoothe, so fine, so stark?"

And the wise screech-owl ventures a word:
  "It's blood, it's human blood!
The living blood that feeds the roots
  Of the shrubs of this neighbourhood."

'Koperkapel' C. Louis Leipoldt
Trans. Guy Butler

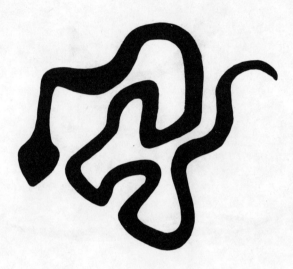

Nyoka huru haizvirumi (nyange yafa neshungu).

A big snake does not bite itself, even if it dies with anger.

An adult should not be overcome by emotions.

Shona

'Erroneous beliefs about this species are legion. Of these, special
mention may be made of the firm belief that it is able to suckle cows,
etc; this is of course manifestly not only untrue but impossible. In
actual fact, these snakes markedly prefer water to milk.'
VFM FitzSimons, *Snakes of Southern Africa,* p300.

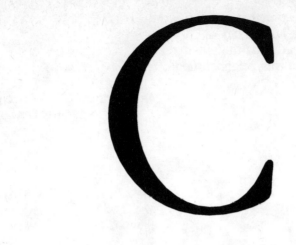

CROCODILE Reptiles of the Family *Crocodylidae.*

NAMES
English: *Nile - or African crocodile*
Afrikaans: *Afrikaanse krokodil*
African: *ingwenya (Z)*
Scientific: *Crocodilus niloticus*

84

DISTRIBUTION: Throughout the African continent, from Upper Egypt to the northern parts of South Africa, and in Madagascar.

DIET: Antelope, but also fish, birds and even insects. Attacks on man are quite common.

FEATURES AND HABITS: Amphibious and confined to rivers, lakes or swamps in or on the banks of which they live. Spend much of their time basking in the sun. They are covered with an armour of ossified, horny plates. They swim by means of lateral movements of their tails with which they also stun their prey. To come within striking distance of animals drinking at the waters edge to do their 'floating-log' act.
Nostrils, eyes and ear openings are so arranged that they project slightly above the water when floating with the rest of the body submerged. The female lays an average of fifty hard-shelled eggs in a shallow excavation on the dry, sandy banks adjoining the habitat. She guards the eggs and opens the nest when she hears the 'cheeping' of the young about to hatch.

HOW DOTH –

How doth the little crocodile
    Improve his shining tail,
And pour the waters of the Nile
    On every golden scale!

How cheerfully he seems to grin,
    How neatly spreads his claws,
And welcomes little fishes in
    With gently smiling jaws!

Lewis Carroll

CROCODILE

I saw you once, half-in half-out
a pit of dirty greenish water.
Walls and bars surrounded you
and children's laughter echoed
emptily through other cages,
through the stink of pissed-on straw.
You lay under a dribbling tap,
a wet plonking on your back
of beaten shoes and handbags.
One bulging green-veined eyeball
slowly opened once or twice.
Was it content or a sleepy drowse
that, with your long travelling mouth set
almost in a smile, you lay so for hours?
I thought you well contained:
in pit, in reptile house, in zoo,
park and town - seas and seas
away from where you chose.
Or didn't it matter, - that anywhere
you would lie so, elbows out,
lizard arms and legs at rest,
snout flat, trunk fatly bulging?
They threw you a calf's head each day.
That did you while you waited
for the delicate horned foot to come
stepping through the grass.
In your blinking eye still waits
a massive writhe and lunge,
the crackle of small bones
and a parting swirl of muddy water.

Rowland Molony

THE CROCODILE

The crocodile is full of spleen:

He mulls the bile of judges.

He purifies his river;
the white corpuscle
devours the red.

His law
is the law of take
and it is just.

The water
thrashes
at his moment of revelation.

Time and he continue.

Bruce Hewett

Uchangotyei kurumwa nengwena makumbno ari mudziva?

Why should you be afraid to be bitten by crocodiles when your legs are
in the pool? Rather persevere than hesitate once you have decided to
do something.

Shona

D

DRAGONFLY *Odonata :* two different groups can be identified; *Zygoptera* and *anisoptera*

NAMES
English: *Dragonfly*
Afrikaans: *naaldekoker*
African: *uzekamanzi (Z)*

DISTRIBUTION: Worldwide except in the polar regions.

DIET: Flying insects, particularly mosquitoes.

FEATURES AND HABITS: Dragonflies are among the largest insects known to have lived. Fossils, some 290 million years old, with a wingspan of 69cm have been found in France. Most obvious characteristics are the four membranous wings, supported by a network of veins, the elongated, often slender bodies, large compound eyes and brilliant colours. The dragonfly is swift of flight and often seen hovering over sheets of water in summer. This predacious insect has biting mouth parts. Its body colour is probably due to a combination of internal pigment, external exudation and light interference. After mating in the air the female lays her eggs in water or inserts them in submerged plant stems. The larvae, called nymphs, are carnivorous and respire by gills.

DRAGON-FLY LOVE

Plated with light I float a thousand-eyed,
On rustling wings of veiny talc to fly,
To kiss in flight the image of my bride
That skims the deep reflection of the sky,
Where finny shoals in shadowy grace repose:
Insects that perish with a tiny cry
Provide the speed with which my body goes
In scaly splendour quadruplaning by.

Giddy with hope I seize my love at noon;
On tremulous waves of fiery air we run,
Long locked in love, across the red lagoon,
Blazing delirious while we whirl as one -
Diamonds melting underneath the moon,
Planets in union going round the sun.

William Plomer

DRAGON-FLY

'Of all the insects it is the dragon-fly of which the poet most frequently
sings; it is the dragon-fly that the sensitive oriental artist depicts on
silk and china or casts in silver or bronze; and it is the dragon-fly that,
as reflected in folklore and colloquialism, catches the small boy's fancy
and at the same time frightens him with fearsome but groundless tales
of having his ears or eyes sewed up by those darning needles, those
horse-stingers, those snake doctors! We might add that these insects
are the most sporting; and he who has ever prided himself on his
wingshooting or his fly casting should try his skill at netting a spirited
and tantalising Aeschnid.' (Klots and Klots. *Living Insects of the
World,* p54.).

DUIKER Subfamily *Cephalophinae*

NAMES
English: *Grey Duiker, Common Duiker*
Afrikaans: *Gewone Duiker*
African: *impunze (Z)*
Scientific: *Sylvicapra grimmia*

DISTRIBUTION: One of the commonest antelopes in southern Africa and found in most of Africa. Other species, such as the Red and Blue Duiker are less common.

DIET: Shoots and leaves of almost all plants. They damage gardens and crops because they nip off growing tips and strip off bark. The Grey Duiker can go without water for long periods, but some other members of the species need water regularly.

FEATURES AND HABITS: Different shades of grey, with some buff or rufous hues, depending on the area. All duikers have a pronounced tuft or crest of long hair on top of the head. This, together with the fact that specimens with one horn missing or malformed are often found, probably explains rock-paintings of 'unicorns'. Most duikers are scrub and forest dwellers but the common duiker is found in all areas where there is some bush or underbrush to provide food and cover. Their furtive, squatting, dodging habits are aptly described by their Afrikaans name, duiker, which means 'diver'. One of the smallest antelopes in Africa, it is a solitary, plucky beast, preyed upon by cheetah, jackal, python, eagles and others. Very often snared by man. They breed throughout the year and a single lamb is born.

A PIECE OF EARTH

The blue duiker, left hindleg
in a poacher's noose held
to a piece of earth by an iron peg,
stands, heart jumping, puzzled;
his scared velvet ears spread
to the sly rustle of leaves and stems;
huge tired eyes probing
the recesses of his epoch's dusk.

He has been snared three days
of sleepless terror; throat scorched with thirst,
tongue thick from rust, dust and blood,
one tiny horn broken from his first
fight with the iron in the earth's skin.
The footloose poacher, long gone
for weeks, has moved on,
will not be returning.

At lengthening intervals
the hare-sized buck gathers himself
for bounding, mouth wide and whistling,
to tow the piece of earth with him.
The wire bites tighter.
Blood flows, clots, runs, congeals
until metal wholly rings on bone.
The earth remains unmoving.

He stops aghast at his noise;
quivering, pants quietly;
resumes his frenzied leaping.
Soon, small herbivorous teeth
will have to grit to gnaw through pain.
Water lies a doubtful day
away: a three-legged stumble through
hyena-patrolled terrain.

Douglas Livingtone

DUIKER DOE

An old half-pay sea captain, shaving one May morning,
His flat brown cheeks half-lathered, saw a mermaid
Riding a unicorn across the satin bay,
Across the empty sea beyond the esplanade;
And left unbuttoned all his tidy day
And left the little squiredom he had made,
Tomato tubs and melon frames he'd planted,
Vanished into his future, sober, spry, enchanted,
And left untenanted the vacant bright May morning.

I read this overnight: this morning I am shaving -
And there, beyond my mirror, not a unicorn
But a duiker doe who primly prunes my roses,
With sly prehensile lip fumbling the shoot and thorn:
Ear-flick and nostril-twitch the lurking fear discloses
With tight-strung nerves across composure drawn.
Rosebud and honeysuckle fed, mild sybarite,
Tiptoe between alarm and appetite -
I watch her, and grimace, and go on shaving.

Quick flux of fear and feed, so odd assorting,
Poised for the sidelong swerve or headlong leap.
Instinct, hallucination - what is it comprehends
Behind my still mirror while the shadows creep?
To hold the timid minutes in close hands
For truth: to love, to know - knowing, to keep:
No subterfuge nor fable to invent,
Unicorn, beast of the virgin girl, guard of the innocent,
On silver snaffle down the morning snorting.

N.H. Brettell

Mhembwe rudzi inozvara ina kazhuma.

The duiker is a kind which brings forth one with a tuft of hair.

Children take after their parents.

Shona

94

E

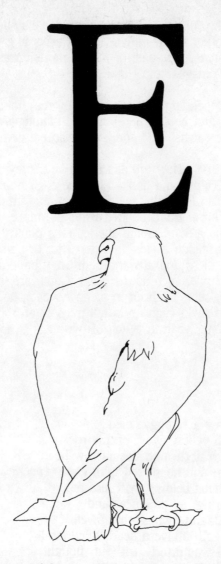

EAGLE Family *Aquilidae* to which Hawks also belong. Thirteen species of true eagles are seen in South Africa, three of which are migrants from Europe and Asia.

NAMES
English: *Eagle; Black, Martial, Fish, Tawny, Bateleur, etc.*
Afrikaans: *Arend; Witkruis-, Breekop-, Vis-, Roof-, Berghaan, ens.*
African: *u-Kosi (X,Z), Ntsu (S)*

DISTRIBUTION: Black, Martial and Fish Eagles are distributed througout southern Africa but other species are scattered according to their preference for drier areas, the coast or mountainous terrain. All thirteen species are seen in Transvaal and Natal.

DIET: Carnivorous. Depending on their size they may take termites, frogs and rodents, dassies and poultry and quite big mammals like baboon and small antelope. Some eat fish and some will also eat carrion.

FEATURES AND HABITS: They are diurnal birds of prey and vary considerably in size, colour and habits. All true eagles have fully feathered legs. When in flight this feature, together with the fact that separate feathers stick out from rounded wingtips, make them easy to identify them from the ground. Some species take poultry and smaller livestock and for this reason eagles are often shot or poisoned. Much of this persecution is ruthless and unwarranted. They have been decimated in settled areas and some, such as the Black Eagle, are threatened with extinction. Eagles are seen singly or in pairs, never in flocks. Their nests are large platforms of sticks high up in tall trees or on rock ledges and are often used year after year. A clutch of two eggs is normal.

EAGLE

In the third wall I saw a scraggy, pied
eagle, watchful, with yellow eyes, on his rock
high on a crag; tough neck; and the narrow head
naked under the sun; and he stirred with every speck
that stirred in the plains below; swift and fell
in his falling; all staring, all patience; and
still, so still on the floating wings that swell
with the slightest breath above a death-filled land.
The small cruel skull was utterly without thought -
and all the way from the eye's unblinking gold
through the scrawny neck above the long wings' fold
down to the very talon, all was taut,
bent as a bow; alone and far he dines,
and even where he's not his ranging terror reigns.

N.P. van Wyk Louw
Trans. Guy Butler

BLACK EAGLE

Everything about him is hieratic:
Egyptian profile and obsidian body
Shaped like the Nile rock-birds
His posture when standing.
Even his flight is a hieroglyphic
On the blue sky. Priestly, too,
Falling on his prey and,
As if in benediction,
Spreading his white cross
Which he folds discreetly back
As he mantles over the kill.
Not the greatest of his species
He wears no crown and yet
Incomparable in flight
Impressive in repose
Regarding whatever holds his gaze
Askance, with a single heliodoric eye.

Charles Eglington

THE EAGLE

Floating in the flat air
he combs the jungle
spread before him, a map.
The eagle reads
and counts the contours
that swallow the shivery rat,
or panicking lizard.
His learned eyes brush
and sift the chaff of life
hidden in still contours.
The eagle reads his map
with cautioned eyes,
eyes that turn over the new leaf
to fan jungle nerves
with blazing claws.

Look, the eagle, spread before empty skies,
his ways are thus,
roaming the sky
reading the jungle
and royal in motioned grace,
while hearts swell and wither
with the flap of mighty wings.

L. wa Kabika and C. Hove

THE EAGLE AND THE SKYDIVER

Like me
the eagle has attained heights
beyond passion.
We are worthy
of our skies assumed.
We fall with death
to befriend life
living the Moment
as we do!
Our land
is the land of evening
after the earthquake's day.
Our skies
are level evening skies.
Sometimes we quicken
on the edge of a greater Mind.
I perceive he has something
to say to me
a silent word of eyes
that tells me not to fall
but soar with him forever.

Bruce Hewett

Ukhoz' olubambayo ngoluzulayo.
The eagle that catches (prey) is the one which wanders.

Just as an eagle cannot expect to get food unless it hunts for it, a person should not expect to get anything unless he works for it.

Zulu

Pabva gondo pagare zizi.
Where the eagle left, the owl sat down.

Where one important person has left or has died, another has taken his place.

Shona

E

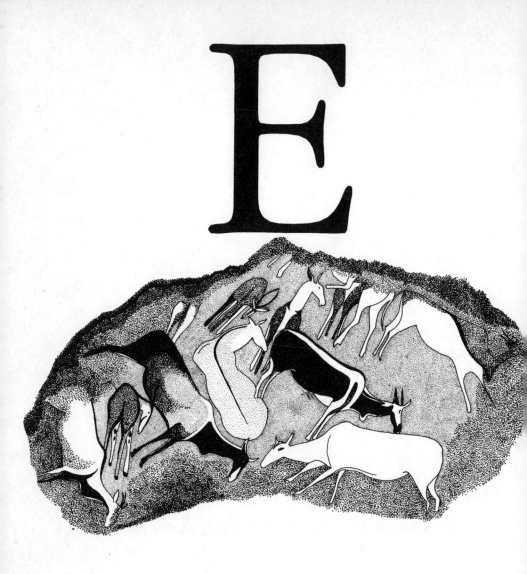

ELAND *Taurotragus oryx*

Names: *English: Eland*
Afrikaans: *Eland*
African: *Impofu (Z)*

DISTRIBUTION: Formerly common from the Cape to the Sudan. Today no longer found south of the Orange River except where they have been re-introduced on to farms.

DIET: They are mainly browsers but also eat young grass and are fond of Acacia pods, wild fruits and berries. In dry areas they will dig up bulbs and roots.

FEATURES AND HABITS: The cattle-like eland is the largest of all antelope. It is pale to rufous-fawn in colour except for old animals who become bluish-grey. Both bulls and cows have prominent dewlaps which are usually provided with tufts of black hair. They prefer open bush country and generally live in small herds. Large scale migrations sometimes take place and at such times as many as 200 animals may be seen together. Eland are gentle-natured animals and although very shy in the wild are easily tamed in captivity. The lion is their principal enemy. Calves are born throughout the year with a peak in early summer, just before the rains.

THE ELAND

That the touch of a diminutive hand
Should cause the eland to leap up grey and red and run
that is the miracle fulfilling itself in the cave

yellow finger red clay that is the miracle
the eland touched into life on a surface of stone
the big yellow pigmy and the little brown eland

the big ochre beast rises up from the dust
and stares at the life composed in paint
from the mouth of the cave by the skew gwarrie bush

a human creature steps out of the low cliff
out to the grey herd far far in the flats
to catch the wind and to shoot the short arrow

to catch the buck with the black horns
the belly a rough grey-red on grey smooth stone
and the strong feet and the short tail and the rippled dewlap

that is the miracle which fulfils itself as the arrow
in the hand which still a hand becomes a brush
a hand which causes rock to live

hand which brings life a living hand
baptises the arrow in venom of snake and poison-bulb
and stretches the bow horizon wide

at the target drawn on the great great sky.

Wilma Stockenström
'Eland' Trans. Guy Butler

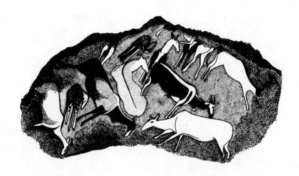

When discussing religion with his Bushman informant in the eighteen-
seventies, magistrate Mr J M Orpen asked 'Where is Kaggen?' (He
spelled it 'Cagn'). The reply was, "We don't know, but the eland do.
Have you not hunted and heard his cry, when the elands suddenly
start and run to his call? Where he is, elands are, in droves like
cattle."

Bushman (Orpen)

102

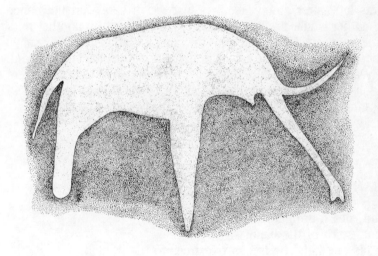

ELEPHANT Order *Proboscidea* to which both the African and Asian elephant belong.

NAMES
English: *African Elephant*
Afrikaans: *Afrikaanse Olifant*
African: *indlovu (Z)*
Scientific: *Loxodanta africana*

DISTRIBUTION: Throughout sub-Saharan Africa, but in South Africa today elephants are found only in the Knysna forests, the Addo bush, northern Zululand and the Transvaal Lowveld.

DIET: They consume as much as 300kg of vegetation per day and feed mainly on grass and reeds. They are also very partial to young shoots and leaves, often breaking a whole tree down to get to these.

FEATURES AND HABITS: The African elephant is larger and has bigger ears than the Asian elephant. It is greyish in colour, but takes on the local soil colour because it covers itself in dust and mud to get rid of ticks and other parasites. It uses its prehensile trunk to get food and water into its mouth. Elephants are gregarious and normally assemble in family groups of about five to fifteen animals, under a matriarch. Usually one calf is born in the early summer, after a gestation of 22 months. Elephants look after group members in need of care - an unweaned calf whose mother is killed will, for instance, be adopted by another nursing cow. They are intelligent and quite tolerant of humans, bulls usually being better-natured than cows. The myth of an elephant 'graveyard' probably arises from the fact that old elephants move to areas where the vegetation is softest, since they are unable to chew hard foods with their deteriorating teeth. It follows that an unusually large number would eventually accumulate in such an area.

ELEPHANT

Elephant, death-bringer!
Elephant, spirit of the bush!
  With his one hand he brings two trees to the ground;
If he had two hands, he would tear the sky like an
    old rag.
Spirit who eats dog!
Spirit who eats ram!
Spirit who eats palm-fruit, thorns and all!
With four pestle-legs he flattens the grass,
Where he walks, the grass cannot stand again.
An elephant is no load for an old man—
Not even for a young man!

Yoruba

ELETELEPHONY

Once there was an elephant,
Who tried to use the telephant -
No! no! I mean an elephone
Who tried to use the telephone -
(Dear me! I am not certain quite
That even now I've got it right.)

Howe'er it was, he got his trunk
Entangled in the telephunk;
The more he tried to get it free
The louder buzzed the telephee -
(I fear I'd better drop the song
Of elephop and telephong!)

Laura E. Richards

ELEPHANT

Slowly the great head turned,
And the late sunlight slept on massive flanks
Like the still slabs of riven krantz,
Immovable, and nonchalantly bearing
The burden of the old enormous lies,
The load of legendary centuries,
The mighty turtle and the seas of milk
On which the old World swam;
And slowly folded back the fluted ears
Like pterodactyl wings drooping to roost.

Slowly the great limbs moved:
The monstrous pistons in the wrinkled sheath,
Unflurried and unhesitating, lift
The huge facade across the afternoon:
Like a great engine, headed north,
With the deliberation of the six-foot wheels
Slides from the vaulted terminus
Down miles of metals through a continent.
Behemoth, baron, lord,

In trigger-fingered World, one creature left unscathed;
Away from us, over the burnt earth, under the prostrate branches,
Casually stripping the green crown from a tree,
Going oblivious, the invulnerable beast.

                                                    N.H. Brettell

ELEPHANT HUNT

Deep within your ancient land we crept
On timid feet, saw emptiness unending,
Lightless, shadow filled and silent kept.
A kingdom marvellous, broad river bending,
Warm as orchid mist and damp with rain.
Slowly through the tangled avenues
The dripping boulevards of your domain
We stumbled, whispering. Fleeting views
Of stumbling apes in upward avalanche
And wide-eyed crashing antelopes released
Our gaze momentarily from splintered branch
And shredded leaf, the crumbs of your repast
An hour old. Your circled languid feet
Left pressured hollows on a moulding floor
And mounded dungheaps steaming still with heat
Set hearts aflame and eyes to strain once more.
We found you in a hall of ancient trees
Which echoed pistol shots of snapping bough,
Shade grey you were, tremendous, such towering frieze
Of tusk agleam, of waving ear, of cow
And calf, of long-lashed eye, we huddled down
Bewildered, filled with awe. On ant-soft tread
You moved towards us, silent, brown on brown,
And so we flung our thundering steels of lead,
Saw hide give up a cloud of river clay,
Saw knees unbend, saw ragged ears on high,
Heard thickets tear, heard echoes fly away
And watched you stagger, crash to earth and lie
Quite still, a silent pile, a hill of dark
Among a wilderness. Slowly folding
Silence captured all; a palace stark

Without a court, a palace garden holding
Emptiness and a king dead on his throne.
We stood bemused, deafened, furtive and alone.

Hjalmar Thesen

TO A DEAD ELEPHANT

Old Python Nose with the wind-rolling ears:
   Hau! I remember it well when you came,
   thin, small, grey, twinkle-eyed, stumbling and lame,
to me, a lone boy with none of the fears
that stalked the elders. Friend, I had no tears
   for both our young losses; but all the same
   you robbed me of those sweet potatoes!
                             Fame
walked with us, both motherless, those coupled-years.

But who can tame the trumpeter, the hill
   who stands invisible with bright old eyes,
so slow, tree-bulky, dangerous and still?
   Why did you leave me to the elders' lies?
Both men, we meet again, but not my will
   wrought this antheap with flies and hamstrung thighs.

Douglas Livingstone

WRITTEN IN AN ELEPHANT'S GRAVEYARD

(for Guy Butler)

What a standing up
what a resurrection
will be here!
The earth quakes
as bones assemble
the character of giants.
Forests of bones arise
with strength enough
to lift the leaves
of every sad autumn.

Great tuskers
assume immortal flesh
beskinned with armour
for Armageddon.
War elephants -
quakers of the Alps -
stand up glowering
everyone a rogue for Christ.
Charge for the last time
the teak beams of Hell.
What a standing up
what a resurrection
will be here!

Bruce Hewett

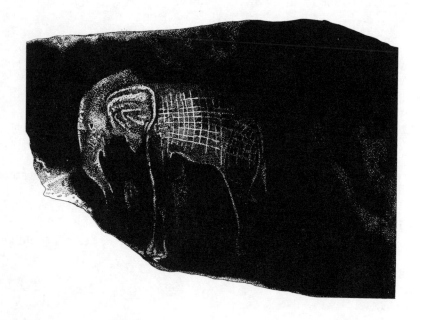

Akukko ndlovu isindwa ngum-boko wayo.
No elephant is overburdened by its own trunk.

A man should be capable of bearing his own troubles.

Xhosa

Indlov' ihlatshwa ngabantu bonke kandukub' iwe.
The elephant is stabbed by all before it falls.

The elephant is a big and strong animal. It always takes some doing to bring an elephant to its knees. The expression is used of a powerful person who would not be easily overcome.

Zulu

Kukpedza simba kunhema nzou dzichauya.
To expend your energy on a rhino when the elephants are coming.

To waste your power on insignificant matters while serious ones lie ahead.

Shona

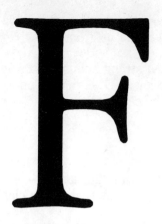

FROG Order *Anura* - the largest order of amphibians. About a hundred different varieties are found in South Africa, four hundred in Africa and twelve hundred in the world.

NAMES
English: *Frog or toad, depending on characteristics. Bull Frog, Mountain Toad, Tree Frog, Platanna, etc. according to species.*
Afrikaans: *Padda - no distinction is made between frogs and toads; brulpadda, blaasop, platanna, etc.*
African: *isele, ingxangxa, ixoxo (Z).*

DISTRIBUTION: Except for the Antarctic, frogs are found almost everywhere in the world; tropical rain forests, high mountains, semi-arid and even arid areas.

DIET: Predators with voracious appetites. Depending on the species, their diet includes insects, such as mosquitoes, as well as their eggs and larvae, snails, ants, termites or worms, etc. and in this they are valuable allies of man.

FEATURES AND HABITS: Most toads and frogs are crepuscular and nocturnal. A great variety of forms, habits and lifestyles have developed. Some spend their lives in the water, some live underground in burrows and never go into water, while others live in trees. The size of anurans varie between 250mm and 11mm. In South Africa, the bull frog, at a maximum of about 190mm is the largest and a 18mm frog found on the Cape Flats is the smallest. Most anurans have the ability to change colour and usually, but not always, poisonous ones are brightly coloured. The most poisonous species in South Africa is the black and scarlet Red-banded frog. Most frogs have smooth skins with mucous glands to keep them moist; in addition to which toads have warty protuberances and swellings on their skins which secrete toxic substances. This secretion irritates the mucous membranes of the eyes, mouth and stomach of an enemy, such as a bird, cat or snake, and is an important defence mechanism. Frogs have long legs which enable them to leap, while toads can only walk or hop. Frogs have teeth in their upper jaws while toads are edentulous. The skin, always moist and richly supplied with deoxygenated blood, is used as a respiratory surface. Anurans are very noisy creatures and each different species has a different call by which it can be identified. Breeding takes place soon after the start of the rainy season. Eggs are laid singly, in clusters or in strings. They are often seen as a jelly-like mass or an albuminous froth on waterside rocks and plants. Females of some species may lay as many as 40 000 eggs per season while others lay only ten or twenty eggs at a time. A free-living tadpole stage is characteristic of the life-cycle of most anurans but in some species this aquatic stage has been eliminated. In South Africa, hibernation during cold winter months is not a common phenomenon. Frogs and toads, however, go into a similar state of torpidity, known as aestivation, during the long dry seasons and droughts and this has saved these water-dependent creatures from extinction.

THE FROG

What a funny bird the frog are
When he stand he sit
Almost
When he jump, he fly
Almost
He ain't got no head hardly
He ain't got no tail hardly either.
He sit on what he ain't got
Almost.

Anonymous

FROGS

Down in the dam various frogs are submitting
Quotations to the evening. Ducks hiss overhead
On fingerwings, turn and land, bringing down
Evening light. The reeds are still.
In there the frogs are winding up to run
At various speeds. Who would think those soft
Wet lumps could grind out noise like miles
Of stony road. Some engage oval gears,
Others talk rubble, a few fat impresarios
Quip wet witticisms from deep among the reeds.
They are plugs for all the holes in this world.
They are water's knots with a throat grown in.
They speak from the bottom of the dam, of
Black ooze, the snail-shell squirm, and the
Pink approach of the barbel's sucking mouth.
Poor frogs: November rains them onto roads,
Splashes them in coloured bags, or stuffs them
Headfirst into the mouths of brown housesnakes.
They are water's only mouth and eyes, come
Straying onto land, forever ushered out of doors
To sit blinking in the wet grass.

Rowland Molony

FROGS

When heaven dissolves in falling rain,
on trees, umbrellas, roofs again,
a stirring moves us in the flood,
    by bog and fen,
    you hear us then,
all cooing like the ringdoves of the mud.

We feel His inspiration,
anew as in creation,
and from primaeval marshes all awake;
    then, little and unwise,
    in praise or blame our cries
resume the uncompleted great debate.

First brightnesses retire
and all is sunk in mire.
While others in their slumber lie withdrawn,
    between the standard reeds
    our city breeds,
we thread the strings of lanterns with our spawn.

Our aim is still the moth -
but God commands in wrath:
'Leap from the brooks, plague house and feast,
    spring from your streams
    to Pharaoh's bed and dreams,
until My captive people are released.'

We who from the slime
turn hill and star to rhyme,
sing from the gurgling marshes in accord,
    through ages in our strophes,
    and antistrophes,
loud Hosannas to the Lord.

D.J. Opperman
Trans. Jean Branford

FROG
   (for Ruth Harnett)

His onepump
nightfall
youngblood gwawking in the bog - no

prince: all
in reach
small flies gulped once

wild, so
serenely;
nothing out of reach,

no excuse, no
magic tightening
his back into the surface of a stone

or log
or frog
or with a leap, into the heartbeat of a man:

man: convex
privacy of chin;
eyes nose mouth turn with it and pause

and haunt the world:
and again and then again
at the brink where the waterlilies lie.

'I am not the turtledove
the ringdove, flying,
the sun on the brink, the lion coming down to drink.'

Said, not by him,
not his words - Splash!
no millenium: it's his place, it stuck to him,

Lamb-lion of the low mud ... he's gone.
O bulging eye.

Sydney Clouts

TO SEPARATE THE TADPOLES FROM THE FROGS

Sleep spawns ideas
like frogs' eggs
in my brain.
Dawn scatters the tadpoles
from their futile nibbling
at some central troutfly...
a game of possibilities
before the statement of life
begins!
This teeming opportunity
happens every day.
Some day I shall
hatch a great frog
whose bravado kick
will span
the cascado of mortal life
going the opposite way.

Bruce Hewett

Akusele lingalunguz' esizibeni salo.
There is no frog that does not peep out of its pool.

Frogs live in the water. From time to time a frog will come up to the surface of the water. That action is regarded by the people as dangerous, for if there is something looking for a frog, the frog betrays its presence by peeping.

The saying means that everyone will take a chance in the hope that it will succeed.

Zulu

115

G

GIRAFFE *Giraffa camelopardalis*

NAMES
English: *Giraffe*
Afrikaans: *Kameelperd*
African: *indlulamithi (Z)*

DISTRIBUTION: Occurs only in Africa, in isolated pockets of open acacia savannah i.e. southern Mozambique, eastern Transvaal, northern Botswana and northern Namibia.

DIET: They are browsers, partial to acacia. The mouth is protected against thorns by a horny layer of skin and thick saliva. Can go without water but drinks regularly when it is available.

FEATURES AND HABITS: It is the tallest animal on earth and has the largest heart, which is necessary to pump the blood some 3 metres up the long neck. What appear to be horns are two bony, skin-covered projections of the skull. They have no vocal chords but are able to make a kind of bleating noise and also snort and grunt. Giraffes are diurnal animals and gregarious. Herds of twenty or more are common. It has an extraordinary, slow-motion gallop, with the neck swinging backwards and forwards in rhythm with the legs, and attains a speed of about 50km per hour over short distances. It is normally very gentle but will defend itself with powerful kicks and also uses its neck as a battering ram. The lion is its most serious enemy but leopards and hyena may also kill calves. Normally one calf is born after a gestation of 15 months.

THE GIRAFFE

A doubtful friend is the Giraffe,
Distrust him when you hear him laugh.

He laughs like people at a ball,
And not because he's pleased at all.

He stretches out his neck like tape,
Until its length precludes escape,

And then he dexterously throws
The window open with his nose.

And if you hide beneath a chair
He finds you out, and pins you there.

George Wyndham

GIRAFFES

Framed in the sedan windows, the tall triangular faces
Watched us with distant interest above the green-
Fringed parasols of the immense acacias
That scattered their point-devise in shady places
        And the heat shimmer lay between.

Out-focused through lorgnette or quizzing-glass,
Neck inter-crossing neck, glance backward from between
Serpentine vertebrae, harmless and mild as doves,
With velvet hornlets topped, leisured they pass,
        Innocent, epicene.

Till with their five attenuated limbs
With gesture of a slowly geared machine,
They pick up distance on an enormous hand,
Outpacing my fantastic synonyms:
        The sedan windows quivered in between.

Slowly the sedans pass:
With lamp-light and link-light bobbing on the strings
Of smooth blond faces down the boulevards,
With paint and patch behind the discreet glass
Attend the whispered tryst, the slow pavane, the cards,
The coy queens and complacent kings,
All the brocaded faded go-betweens,
And centuries remote beyond the sedan windows.

Your grave quaint harlequins, to deceive us
With the gay curves of kirtle and crinoline
In a grey wilderness. Reluctantly leave us,
While the incessant grasshoppers scissor away the minutes;
        O lost arcadian scene,

O happy groves: centaur and unicorn prances
Across the hourless wastes that lie between
Our watchful present and the wistful bygones,
When the bland century and our budding fancies
        Were both eighteen.

                       N.H. Brettell

GROOM: GIRAFFE: EMPEROR
(from a 15th Century Chinese painting on silk)

Both sceptical and superstitious the black-bearded groom
Can't quite believe that his foreign charge is real,
Except when, as now, instead of lolloping after,
It fixes all four feet in their tracks and jerks
That long neck back. The long rein, losing its slack,
Almost dislocates his clavicle.

So he turns, this stocky groom, turns in his tracks
To utter an oath both bestial and blasphemous;
Which oath has a long way to go, all up the long rein
To reach those ears perched like birds
On the heaven-high head,
That sensitive nostril sniffing down,
Thin lips curled to reveal teeth gnashing,
Long-lashed almond eyes in a questioning frown
That fine, intelligent, highborn, foreign face
Objecting to being led by him, him, chief groom
To the Emperor-of-all-the-Chinas.

Surely the merchants supplying the royal menagerie
Have over-reached themselves, have gone too far this time,
To Africa, yes Africa,
Returning with this - this? - this?
Is it an animal, or a god?
Either? neither? both?

I know about animals, I do, says that groom.
But as for you, you bastard between a camel and a leopard
With your hide all hidden in sinister hexagons -
Why, if a god, did you get your divine self caught?
To amuse yourself with the sight of mortals
Pretending to be gods? But if you're merely a beast,
God help us both if you curl that lip
And sneer at his Celestial Highness.
Give me a hungry lion any day.

The celestial Emperor looked long at the long creature
Three times as tall as a man, and then he said,
It is the holiest of beasts, its head being closest to heaven,
It is sweet of soul, its hide is a golden honeycomb.
Let it be fed forever on vegetables from my gardens.

How long did the African exile survive, bored,
Stiff-necked from stooping
To a diet of fresh imperial greens?
Did he dream of days when he'd gazed at the sun
Rising over a sea of acacia tops,
Ignorant that it was already setting
Over this imperial menagerie,
These staring crowds, these makers of lucid porcelains,
This delicate painter on silk?

Guy Butler

GIRAFFE

From DREAMING SPIRES

The City of Giraffes! - a People
Who live between the earth and skies,
Each in his lone religious steeple,
Keeping a light-house with his eyes:

Each his own stairway, tower, and stylite,
Ascending on his saintly way
Up rungs of gold into the twilight
And leafy ladders to the day:

Chimneys of silence! at whose summit,
Like storks, the daydreams love to nest;
The Earth, descending like a plummet
Into the oceans of unrest,

They can ignore - whose nearer neighbour
The sun is, with the stars and moon
That on their hide, with learned labour,
Tatooed the hieroglyphic rune.

Muezzins that from airy pylons
Peer out above the golden trees
Where the mimosas fleece the silence
Or slumber on the drone of bees:

Nought of this earth they see but flowers
Quilting a carpet to the sky
To where some pensive crony towers
Or Kilimanjaro takes the eye.

Their baser passions fast on greens
Where, never to intrude or push,
Their bodies live like submarines,
Far down beneath them, in the bush.

Around their head the solar glories,
With their terrestrial sisters fly -
Rollers, and orioles, and lories,
And trogons of the evening sky.

Their bloodstream with a yeasty leaven
Exalts them to the stars above
As we are raised, though not to heaven,
By drink - or when we fall in love.

By many a dismal crash and wreck
Our dreams are weaned of aviation,
But these have beaten (by a neck!)
The steepest laws of gravitation.

Some animals have all the luck,
Who hurl their breed in nature's throat -
Out of a gumtree by a buck,
Or escalator - by a goat!

When I have worked my ticket, pension,
And whatsoever I can bum,
To colonise the fourth dimension,
With my Beloved, I may come,

And buy a pair of stilts for both,
And hire a periscope for two,
To vegetate in towering sloth
Out here amongst these chosen few ...

Roy Campbell

CONVERSATION WITH A GIRAFFE
AT DUSK IN THE ZOO

Hail, lofty,
necking quizzically
through the topgallant leaves
with your lady.

No good making eyelashes at
the distance from me to you
though I confess I should like
to caress your tender horns
and toboggan down your neck,
perhaps swing on your tail.

Your dignity fools no one;
you get engagingly awkward
when you separate and collapse
yourself to drink;
and have you seen
yourself cantering?

Alright, alright, I know
I'm standing still,
squat-necked, so-high.

Just remember there's one or two
things about you too, hey,
like, like, birds now;
they fly much higher.

Douglas Livingstone

Apart from the mention of the giraffe as a member of the team that
had to rescue Kaggen from the rockfall when he visited the dassies, the
only folklore relevant to giraffe that has been published was recorded
by Doman among the Bushmen of the eastern Kalahari. He wrote that
the Southern Cross is referred to as the "giraffe star" (Doman, 1925).
Various groups of Bushmen had a particular interest in the heavenly
bodies and there is a good deal of relevant folklore. One writer on the
art, Erik Holm, takes the view that there is a close relationship
between it and the heavens (Holm, 1961). He sees an engraving of a
giraffe in the Transvaal Museum, Pretoria, as straining upward towards
the sky rather than in the more mundane act of browsing for food from
the top of a tree, which would occur to more prosaic observers.

Woodhouse p.49

123

GUINEA-FOWL Family *Numididae.*

NAMES
English: *Guinea-fowl*
Afrikaans: *Tarentaal*
African: *Impangele (Z,X) Khaka (S)*

124

DISTRIBUTION: Of the five genera, two occur in South Africa and are widespread over the African continent, two are confined to West Africa and one to East Africa.

DIET: A mixed diet of seeds, grains, vegetable matter, insects, snails.

FEATURES AND HABITS: They are fairly large birds and decidedly reluctant to fly, but are great runners. Graphite-grey in colour, most have white or pale blue spots and/or stripes. The head of the crowned guinea-fowl is naked except for a horny casque which may differ slightly between species. The crested guinea-fowl has a topknot of feathers. They are gregarious birds and may form flocks of hundreds, except during the breeding season when they pair off to form family groups. They have no spurs and use their beaks for defense and fighting amongst themselves. The crowned guinea-fowl likes thorny scrub and savannah veld near rivers. They are extremely wily and if threatened will scatter and hide most successfully in trees, grass or bushes. Flocks roost in trees at night. Six to eight uncommonly hard eggs are laid in a grass-lined hollow in the ground, during the rainy season.

GUINEAFOWL

While dusk shades quickly fall
a guineafowl
utters his agonising wail
like a grating barrow wheel.

He seeks, though it is far too late,
a mate
to share his tree, and so make less
night's loneliness.

Together in a gloss-leaf-tree they'll share
sleep mingled with dreams and fear,
and at the approach of ruin
not die alone.

I took aim; with the knell
one fell;
the other sped with violent flight
into the night.

Totius
Trans. Guy Butler

Akusua 'Nowa

They say the guinea-fowl lays her treasure
Where only she can find it.
Akosua 'Nowa is a guinea-fowl:
Go tell her, red ant upon the tree.

I met Akosua 'Nowa this morning;
I greeted:
    Akosua, how is your treasure?
She looked me slowly up and down,
She sneered:
    The man is not yet here who'll find it!

Akosua 'Nowa has touched my manhood;
Tell her, red ant upon the tree:
If she passes this way I am gone,
I am gone to load my gun.

No matter how hidden deep her treasure,
By my father's coffin I swear
I'll shoot my way to it this day;
Son of the hunter king
    There is liquid fire in my gun!

Joe de Graft

Mukuru mukuru hanga haigari bvunde.
A great one is a great one, a guinea fowl does not sit on a cornplant.

A young person should respect elders.

Shona

126

H

HIPPOPOTAMUS *Hippopotamus amphibius*

NAMES
English: *Hippopotamus*
Afrikaans: *Seekoei, Nylperd*
African: *imvubu (Z)*

127

DISTRIBUTION: Formerly in almost all rivers and pools from the Cape to Egypt. Today hippos are found only in the northern and eastern parts of South Africa and in central Africa.

DIET: Grasses and other riverine vegetation. They also eat crops planted near rivers.

FEATURES AND HABITS: Hippos normally form herds of between ten and forty animals. They spend most of the day in the water but cannot stay underwater for longer than about five minutes. They swim around, walk along clearly defined underwater paths, or doze in heaps in shallow water or on sandbars in the river. At nightfall they come ashore to feed and when food is scarce may walk up to 30km before returning to the water by dawn. An adult hippo eats as much as 130kg of vegetation per night. Because it destroys crops it is relentlessly hunted by man, but is also sought after for its meat, fat and hide. When left alone it is quite a placid beast. However, during the mating season violent fights are common, amid ear-shattering grunts and roars. Mortal wounds are sometimes inflicted on adversaries with the shear-like canines. A reddish, glandular secretion of the skin is erroneously called, 'bloody sweat'. A cow usually gives birth to a single calf which can swim within minutes and is able to suckle under water but must come up frequently for air.

Between the years 1927 and 1931 the epic journey of Huberta, the wandering hippo, made headlines across the world. For no apparent reason she decided to trek south along the east coast, from Zululand to King William's Town. *En route* she called on many towns and even paraded down the streets of Durban. Her journey ended tragically when she was shot at the Keiskamma River by three hunters who were later fined R25 each for killing royal game. Her mounted remains can today be seen in the Kaffrarian Museum in King William's Town.

THE HIPPOPOTAMUS

I shoot the hippopotamus
   with bullets made of platinum
Because if I use leaden ones
   his hide is sure to flatten 'em.

Hilaire Belloc

A Dirge

[To be sung to slow drumbeats at ten-second intervals]

Tell them tell it to them
That we the children of Ashiagbor's house
Went to hunt; when we returned,
Our guns were pointing to the earth.
We cannot say it; someone say it for us.
Our tears cannot fall,
We have no mouths to say it with.
We took the canoe, the canoe with sandload
They say the hippo cannot overturn.
Our fathers, the hippo has overturned our canoe.
    We come home
Our guns pointing to the earth.
Our mother, our dear mother
Where are our tears, where are our tears.
Give us mouth to say it, our mother.
We are on our knees to you,
We are still on our knees.

Kofi Awoonor

THE HIPPOPOTAMUS

Behold the hippopotamus!
We laugh at how he looks to us,
And yet in moments dank and grim
I wonder how we look to him.
Peace, peace, thou hippopotamus!
We really look all right to us,
As you no doubt delight the eye
Of other hippopotami.

Ogden Nash

129

THE HABITS OF THE HIPPOPOTAMUS

The hippopotamus is strong
    And huge of head and broad of bustle;
The limbs on which he rolls along
    Are big with hippopotamuscle.

He does not greatly care for sweets
    Like ice cream, apple pie, or custard,
But takes to flavour what he eats
    A little hippopotomustard.

The hippopotamus is true
    To all his principles, and just;
He always tries his best to do
    The things one hippopotomust.

He never rides in trucks or trams,
    In taxicabs or omnibuses,
And so keeps out of traffic jams
    And other hippopotamusses.

                        Arthur Guiterman

DAWN HIPPO

The size of a cavern for men to crouch in
by fire trickling small;
for demons uttered by name
to crowd like tropical thunder
and crackle against the wall,

he domes the birth of day;
built moving on the river,
shrubless mound of weighty sheen,
a large derisive slope
hammering back each ray,
he floats his quiet hilltop
he sizes up the morning;
a zone of bubbles happens round his head,
streaks of his glitter spear them dead,
breaking the break of day.

A fine froth scums his sides like primitive acid,
birds with sharp beaks fly over him;
he bulges landward
choosing a shelved approach,
the water shallows where he wants it to,
pushes in savage rings that smash
high reeds and rock the river. Mud swarms,
mud slimes his paddling belly as he climbs
heavily wagging the water away.
The full ridiculous splendour mobs the stones:
thunder and lightning jostle on his bones.

Sydney Clouts

BELLOWING HIPPOPOTAMUS
Blue faience, Egypt 1600 BC British Museum

Ancient Gyppo
loud-mouthed hippo
of blue faience

from what dark tomb
ridiculous
Lazarus
you've come
to bellow down our doom.

Unlike Eliot
world-weary that a wheel should turn
you do not
yawn
at dawn
nor grind out flinty blues
like Peat Heaney or Hawk Hughes.

Your belly-head shouts
life sans end
raises
pristine praises
like my friend
Clouts.

Guy Butler

131

THE HIPPOPOTAMUS

Out of the Zulu bush one day she came,
Without a by-your-leave, it was good-bye
To the hills of Mapamula, the herd and St. Lucia Bay,
Bellow on the wind and dust in the air,
Through broken mealies, the shattered stalks of cane,
Into our world the hippopotamus came.

Two years the journey, two thousand miles
In bush and swamp, cities, the pages of Punch
And the Times, stirred by ancestral memories, they said,
Searching for a long-lost ego, though once at night
In the dead-quiet street and the window's light,
She saw herself whole and took fright,

But never turned back to the past, the taste
Came soon for lights and fame, one day
At noon from the river's bed late rising,
She walked the square with councillor and mayor
And ate three fields of Pondo's fare, who thought
Thus to placate a much-feared witch.

Ours the accolade came next, the royal game, we too
Made much of her who on dignity and maize grew fat,
At many a muddy spa taking the waters, the sophisticate
Was quite unprepared for the denouement;
In the morning papers, with some surprise, we read
Of a sticky end, at Keiskama, two bullets in the head.

Questions in Parliament and mourning, the assassins
Brought to court, there was nothing mean, I remember
About the passing of Huberta, the celebrity's head
Stood firm on the courtroom table, later for posterity
With its nether self rejoined, was put down for parade
Here in the museum at Kingwilliamstown.

Now twenty five years later as we stand, my child,
You in another generation, would that I could
Draw you but back beyond the taxidermist's art,
To where once and for once the fabulous tale came true,
When the great beast walked each night through the nursery dream
Only to leave, when daylight came, a garden of wrecked cabbages.

Roy Macnab

THE HIPPOPOTAMUS

*And when this epistle is read among you, cause that
it be read also in the church of the Laodiceans*

The broad-backed hippopotamus
Rests on his belly in the mud;
Although he seems so firm to us
He is merely flesh and blood.

Flesh and blood is weak and frail,
Susceptible to nervous shock;
While the True Church can never fail
For it is based upon a rock.

The hippo's feeble steps may err
In compassing material ends,
While the True Church need never stir
To gather in its dividends.

The 'potamus can never reach
The mango on the mango-tree;
But fruits of pomegranate and peach
Refresh the Church from over sea.

At mating time the hippo's voice
Betrays inflexions hoarse and odd,
But every week we hear rejoice
The Church, at being one with God.

The hippopotamus's day
Is passed in sleep; at night he hunts;
God works in a mysterious way--
The Church can sleep and feed at once.

I saw the 'potamus take wing
Ascending from the damp savannas,
And quiring angels round him sing
The praise of God, in loud hosannas.

Blood of the Lamb shall wash him clean
And him shall heavenly arms enfold,
Among the saints he shall be seen
Performing on a harp of gold.

He shall be washed as white as snow,
By all the martyr'd virgins kist,
While the True Church remains below
Wrapt in the old miasmal mist.

T.S. Eliot

Izinyane lemvubu kalidliwanga yingwenya kwacweb' iziziba.
The calf of a hippo was never eaten by a crocodile and the pools
remained clear.

Crocodiles and hippopotami live in the water. The crocodile, if it should
ever eat the hippo calf, must expect trouble from the parent. The water
cannot be clear because of the blood of the calf, and also because of
the fight with the parent.

Therefore, when one does something which hurts extremely, one
should expect vengeance to follow.

Zulu

HYENA Family *Hyaenidae* - three living species

NAMES
English: *Striped, Spotted and Brown Hyena*
Afrikaans: *Gestreepte, Gevlekte en Bruin Hiena (Strandwolf of*
            Strandjut)
African: *impisi, bheka (Z)*
Scientific: *Striped - Hyaena hyaena Spotted - Crocuta crocuta Brown -*
            Hyaena brunnea

DISTRIBUTION: The Striped Hyena occurs in East and North-East Africa, Arabia and India. The Spotted Hyena was once common throughout sub-Saharan Africa. Today it is found mainly in the less civilised northern regions of South Africa and further north although it is probably still the most numerous of the large African carnivores. The Brown Hyena is found only in southern Africa and used to be common along the coasts. Recently its distribution has shrunk rapidly.

DIET: They are carnivores who eat a great deal of carrion but also a variety of other food items such as birds, insects, fish, reptiles and even fruit.

FEATURES AND HABITS: The spotted hyena has round ears and is yellowish buff to tawny in colour with irregular spotted markings on a coarse but short coat. The other two species have pointed ears, longer, shaggier coats of varying shades of ashy-brown with some stripes on the legs and hindquarters. The largest species is the spotted hyena who often kills brown hyenas. Brown and striped hyenas are however, better adapted to harsh environmental conditions and a less reliable food supply. Hyenas are mainly nocturnal and lie up in shady areas during the day. The spotted female is larger than the male, and dominant. In this species external sexual organs appear to be the same in the male and female and there is an erroneous belief that they are hermaphrodites. Hyenas form clans of three to fifteen animals in established territories. Although known as scavengers, they are extremely efficient predators of smaller and even large herbivores. The spotted hyena is also quite capable of driving other predators away from a catch. The eerie wailing howl of the spotted hyena is characteristic of the African bush and its chuckles, groans and demoniacal laughter when excited is legend-provoking and explains why an aura of superstition surrounds it. By contrast the other species are much quieter. An average of two cubs are born and for some months after birth they are cared for in communal dens.

OLD TIKA

'And so, remembering Umtali, Tika came back to seek the dead
trek-oxen' — Native Story.

Staring at every shadow, starting at every sound;
Raising his nose to the chilly night, sinking it now to the
ground;
Craning his head from side to side; faltering, nervous and
lame;
Back by a half-forgotten path, the old hyena came.

    The span-less wagons block'd the roads,
        New dead the cattle lay,
    When from the North the dread disease
        Swept down, Umtali way.
    The rinderpest swept down and past,
        And travell'd to the South —
    And Tika lived the life he loved,
        The fresh bone in his mouth.

    The vultures sat on every tree
        To watch a dying beast,
    At night the grey hyenas came
        And scrambled for the feast.
    But now green mealie-fields had grown
        Upon the quarantine —
    Nothing remain'd to Tika now
        To show what once had been.

    'Aha! These fields are green and new,
        The smell of man is here!
    The smell of bone and hide is gone:
        The breeze is fresh and clear;
    The roads are new, I cannot find
        The tracks I used to tread
    In coming from the kloof above
        To seek the newly dead.

'Who-o-ee! These hills are all too cold,
   And I'll go back again —
Back to the warm dry-river beds,
   To the bush-veld and the plain.
Tika is cold (too cold — too cold
   This bitter East wind blows!)
And he'll go back to the warmer North
   Where the great Zambesi flows.'

Gasping in fear at a passing mouse, grasping a whiten'd bone;
Splashes of yellow on dirty grey; evil and sullen and lone;
Craning his head from side to side; drooping his nose to the
   scent;
Back by a half-forgotten path, the old hyena went ...

Kingsley Fairbridge

WITCHCRAFT

The hyena makes the race-course steed
a false pretender to speed
at one thousand kilometres to the hour
he is supersonic

To sway the course of the wind
is to say no to human arrogance
trapped in sleep and midnight
and yes to the appetite for flesh
Laughter is triumph at the graveside
seeing the mourner and the joker and the chieftain
preside over an empty burial
after the witches' midnight party has emptied
the carcass.

Musaemura Zimunya

138

Chakakodza bere mapfupa.
What fattened the hyena are the bones. What is useless to me is
valuable to another.

Shona

When a leopard asked the guineafowl to give it spots, the test was that
the leopard had to guard her eggs without eating them. This the
leopard did, and received her spots. When the hyena was put to the
same test he did not show the same self-restraint. The result is evident
in its few, ugly spots.

Hyena is the witches' most common familiar associate - a symbol of
any strong and violent desire. Where passions rage beyond control the
way is open to black magic, *uroyi*, that which Taylor in *The Primal
Vision* describes as 'the active embodiment of that brooding anger which
in Africa is the essence of sin'.

I

IMPALA *Aepyceros melampus*

NAMES
English: *Impala, springbok of the Lowveld.*
Afrikaans: *Rooibok, impala.*

DISTRIBUTION: Tropical savannah, from Northern Zululand and Mozambique in the east through the Eastern and Northern Transvaal and Botswana to northern Namibia and northwards to the southern Congo.

DIET: Impala eat an extremely large range of vegetable matter, being both grazers and browsers. They are dependent on the availability of water.

FEATURES AND HABITS: Only the males have horns and they are slightly heavier of build than the females. They are the finest jumpers in Africa and when alarmed or playful may jump three metres in height and up to 12 metres in length with effortless ease. Impala are gregarious creatures and can be found in herds of up to a hundred animals. During the rut intense fighting, which may result in serious injury and even death, goes on among the rams. Impala are the most abundant animals in the Kruger Park where their main enemies are leopards, cheetah and wild dogs. Young impala are also caught by spotted hyenas, jackal and python. Lions find them too elusive and alert but are occasionally successful. A single lamb is born during the early summer.

HERD OF IMPALA

If I close my eyes I can hear them:
A herd of impala, leaping
Across a clearing level as a beach
Strewn with burnt mopani branches turning yellow.

I would go a long way to hear that sound,
A whoosh, a whisper like a thin sword from its scabbard,
A sound like the gleam of a bayonet on night guard,
The far-off rustle of bushes being brushed on soft ground.

They break like pieces from a noiseless grenade,
Death-dealing armour, bullets fired from a rubber gun,
Arcs from each day's birthday of the sun.
Or calling lovers, the final hiss of the last train.

Their horns are lancers on patrol, pennantless thorns
in winter,
The shaking of nude pines in torches of frost,
Brown waves, forever duplicated trough on trough,
Dropping trophies on the beaches, butt ends from the
ocean and fins.

Yet, not so beauiful; unlike hunters I cannot discriminate
The off-cuts for the hunting lodge, the plungers for museums.
I am a marksman only in values of humanness--
The wires upon their bones, the scars of traps, the
final helplessness as bait.

Colin Style

Ungexoshe mpalambili.
You cannot chase two gazelles.

This saying means that one should do one thing at a time. If one
chases a gazelle, and then when another gazelle appears one tries to
chase them both, the result will be a complete failure.

Zulu

Ere phala ele khubidu gale, ebile u e tlotsa lecoku.
The impala is naturally red, yet you smear it with red ochre.
Would you dye a raven black?

Sechuana

142

J

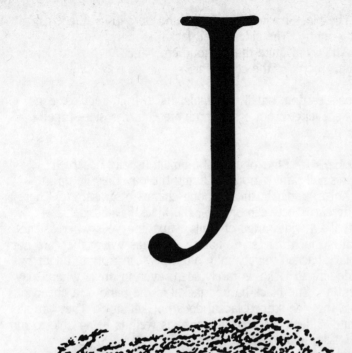

JACKAL Family: *Canidae* Subfamily: *Caninae,* to which foxes also belong. In South Africa there are two species of jackals and foxes respectively.

NAMES:
Depends on the species referred to;
English: *Jackal; Black-backed, Side-striped, etc.*
Afrikaans: *Rooijakkals, Witkwasjakkals, ens.*
African: *iqile (Z)*

DISTRIBUTION: The black-backed jackal is found only in southern Africa and prefers open country. The side-striped jackal is more widely distributed over Africa but quite rare in southern Africa. It prefers denser bush and the wetter parts of the continent.

DIET: Omnivorous - carrion, small mammals, mice, fruit, reptiles, eggs, etc. Both species scavenge from other carnivores but the side-striped jackal to a lesser extent.

FEATURES AND HABITS: Shy, nocturnal animals usually observed singly, in pairs or small family groups. During the day they lie up in disused antbear holes, under bushes, among clumps of grass, etc. There are important differences between species; the black-backed jackal is extremely noisy with a wide range of wails, yaps and yells whereas the side-striped jackal is much quieter by nature. In areas where they are not persecuted the black-backed variety may often be seen trotting about by day while the side-striped jackal is rarely seen, even in areas where they are relatively plentiful. The black-backed jackal is the bane of a sheep farmer's life while the side-striped jackal does not kill stock. They are all very intelligent and difficult to catch in traps, as well as being able to run surprisingly fast. Jackal pairs remain together for years. Up to three pups are born in holes, caves or crevices. They are frequently moved to other holes and both parents help to feed the pups.

THE JACKAL'S LAMENT

I am the one whom the lynx derides,
for I am not cunning, cha, cha!

I am the one whom the cheetah mocks:
'The jackal is he who is slow.'

I am the one whom the ostrich kicks,
whom the lion chases away.

The hyena growls when I come near:
'The jackal is he who eats last.'

Arthur Markowitz

SHE-JACKAL

As the sun fell west he composed himself
against a pinetree bole, happily smooth
a yard above the soft sprung-needle ground
and punched open one of his two beercans.

The hillside sloped sharply and as he lay
propped, sipping and watching the purple hills
with their horizon-long yellowred banners
silently snapping and cracking on crests,
all convex and magnified, almost still,
the other side of the deepshadowed valley,
he saw a shamelessly feminine curved
African — usually so male and wrinkled —
blatant under the first opened stars.

Evilly panting and smiling, a jackal
stood near: razor ribs, warty shrivelled dugs,
hourglass loins and lean wire legs quivering;
the plump feeding ticks studding her bare flanks.
They looked at each other, obviously
disliking what they saw, both warily
tensed, although she retained her polished smile;
he, measuring jumps from her and his stick.

So, you mangy chewer of carrion,
he thought it directly and impolitely,
campfollower of filthy offal-thieves,
what the hell are your drooling over, bitch?
this meat is alive with a nearly full
tin of chemical malt in its right hand.

She made no reply so he flung it hard
and inaccurately and she was gone
apparently without moving; the tin
fanned arcs of liquid silver an instant
of flight against the exhausted sunset.

He got up stiffly and climbed higher, pillared
on the one hand by his staff of bamboo;
in the other, his remaining beercan.
From up there, there might be some sunset left.

Douglas Livingstone

KOROKEN THE JACKAL

Koroken, the jackal, is he who begs.
He begs with uplifted tongue.
He whines, with uplifted tongue he whines.
Indeed, he begs when he howls.

He whines when he begs for springbok flesh.
He, from the leopard begs flesh.
He whines, he howls that he also may eat,
with uplifted tongue he begs.

He begs when the lion has killed a gnu.
Koroken whines for some flesh.
The lion is angry: the lion growls.
The leopard is angry: he grunts.

But Koroken, the jackal, he is the one
who whines and howls for his food.
He fears not a little; he runs away,
he begs with uplifted tongue.

Arthur Markowitz

Siyoze sihlangan' okhalweni lwezimpungushe.
We shall eventually meet in the plain of the jackals.

This is a serious threat. The plain of the jackals is a wilderness where only wild beasts are found, and where one may not expect to get help from anyone. If one should be disabled there, the wild beasts will consume him.

Zulu

Bophokoje ba ba nkgoe ba itsanye ka mebala.
Grey jackals know each other by their speckles.
All flesh consorteth according to its kind, and a man will cleave to his like.

Sechuana

147

KUDU *Tragelaphus strepsiceros*

NAMES:
English: *Kudu*
Afrikaans: *Koedoe*
African: *bheka (Z)*

DISTRIBUTION: Widely distributed throughout southern Africa, northwards across the continent up to the equator, and then along its eastern side as far as Ethiopia and the Sahara.

DIET: They are browsers with an amazingly varied diet - shoots and leaves (even of exotic plants poisonous to other animals), wild fruits, seed pods and most agricultural crops.

FEATURES AND HABITS: The magnificent three-spiralled horns of the male adult kudu is its most distinctive feature. The horns keep growing throughout the animal's life and are an indication of its age. Kudu are normally found in small herds of six to ten animals. They prefer well-bushed, broken hilly country where they feed in the early morning and late afternoon, lying up in the shade during the heat of the day. They are wary and inoffensive by nature but during the rut bulls may fight fiercely for control of the breeding herds. They jump fences of up to 3 metres with great ease and being extremely fond of most crops, can become a problem in some agricultural areas. Calves are born throughout the year but the main calving season is in summer. Because their meat is particularly good, they were ruthlessly hunted down in the past but enjoy some protection today.

ON CLOUDS

Disturbed, the kudu are running
five cows, one pregnant, and in
the lead, ducking under branches,
a bull, 5 feet at the shoulder, a blanched
lance-corporal's chevron between his eyes,
muzzle outthrust and the long spirals
of horn laid along his back
to meet, curled forward and similarly stacked,
his tail; rocking up the hill, fleeing
but with an air of tall dignity;
surefooted as small grey clouds slide
scudding up a wooded hillside.

It is impossible to punch a small hole,
grease- and cordite-stained, into all
this cloudy elegance: impossible I say — they
tame so easily — and pulsing now, grey
like clouds, repulse the sort of vapourization
known, among others, to the Sonderkommando.

Of course, these clouds are but kudu, true:
those other clouds only Jews.

Douglas Livingstone

TO A DEAD KOODOO

In the dappled morning of this land
With its dim ghost mists and its blue stills,
Its bush tangles and its trodden sand,
There is so great a love just now that the hills
Become soft meadows and the wilderness
Is hushed like a sleepfilled garden lawn
With marble lions, imagined leopards and careless
Scattered python toys. Those zebras drawn
In a crisscrossed puzzle are a circus pair
And that lone vulture spiralling high
Is a boy's kite harmless as the air,
Taut upon its string, a hissing sigh
Encircling idly on its seeing wings.
Reality has fled from this bee-filled shadow
With its light bars and its soft un-jungle things,
Its berry-dropping birds; love is aglow
My beautiful Africa, love for the proud bull
Dead in the grass at my feet with his wide horns
And his soft nose; sleek, wonderful,
Bred to the grey thickets and the white thorns,
Rolled in bushveld dew and washed by the dust
Of galloping hooves. Joy and sorrow come
As strangers here where nights are a thin crust
Of safety and days are sleep or hunger or some
Small pleasure of river and sun. I came to kill
But I bring sorrow too and joy and a love

To your death that the lion can never know, nor will
The leopard, nor the python, nor the high vulture above.

Hjalmar Thesen

Most regrettably, we know practically nothing from the published folklore which is derived mainly from Bushmen who came from parts of the country where the habitat was not of the well-wooded kind preferred by kudu.

This is really a great loss because the number of paintings of kudu from the Transvaal northwards across the Limpopo is considerable.

Woodhouse

Go kgola naka loa tholo.
To cut off the horn of a koodoo.
A tough job.

Sechuana

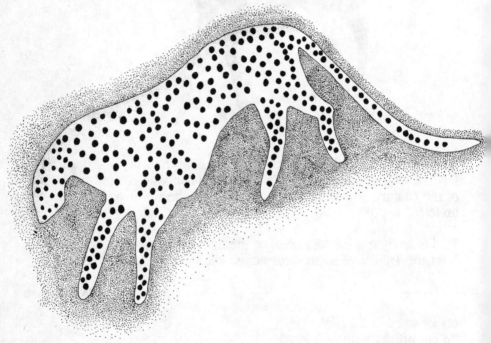

LEOPARD *Panthera pardus*

NAMES
English: *Leopard*
Afrikaans: *Luiperd, Tier*
African: *ingwe, ingwavu (Z)*

152

DISTRIBUTION: All over Africa but rarely in the interior of southern Africa. Also in Asia, Sri Lanka and Malaysia. It frequents the denser bush, whether it be in rocky, mountainous surroundings or in savannah bushveld. It also occurs in primary forests.

DIET: The leopard is carnivorous and eats what it finds in the area in which it lives. It does eat livestock and dogs but this is uncommon. Dassies, baboons, antelopes, game birds, rodents and even reptiles and fish make up its usual fare. This variety of diet has helped the leopard to survive in areas where other predators have long since disappeared.

FEATURES AND HABITS: The leopard is a powerfully-built spotted cat with baleful, pale greenish-yellow eyes. Most of its spots are arranged in rosette-like clusters of three to six. It is a secretive and rather quiet beast, especially where it is persecuted, and spends the day lying up in undergrowth, caves or extended along the branches of tall trees. It hunts at night by stalking its prey or pouncing on it from a tree. When it has had its fill it pulls the remains high up into a tree to keep it out of the reach of other predators. Leopards are solitary creatures but sometimes move about in pairs or with their young. Fighting amongst them is rare except when courting or mating. An average of two to three cubs are born and they remain with the mother for almost two years. It will almost always retreat when humans approach, except if it or its young are threatened.

LEOPARD

Famine drives him from his sovereign rock
To snarl and choke on the fetal
Stench of man and tainted flock.
Hunger gives him dignity, and rage
Contempt: in fear sharper than
His own, men hunt him and assuage
A lust, in him supreme; with awe
They see how, even dead, the sleek
And branded body glows with more
Than feral beauty: in death he still
Lurks within the precincts of their law,
Menacing and augural.

Charles Eglington

153

LEOPARD

See the golden Leopard with the spots!
The golden cat of the cliffs!
See the Leopard with the bulging cheeks,
The golden Leopard with the wide face, I-Fear-
    Nothing,
The particoloured one, I-Climb-Into-A-Small-Tree
I rip off the eyebrows!
Clawer am I, dig my nails in deep,
My enemies I leave behind, saying
'This was not one leopard but ten!'
Mr Claws, Scratch-For-Yourself,
Even a strong man is not ashamed to howl when
    clawed!
Leopards of the Tlokwa country,
Wild cat with the wide face,
We eat the wild antelope and the tame cattle.
The great golden spotted one,
Lone outlaw who brings thousands to him by his art,
Whose victim goes off with his scalp over his eyes,
Leopard of many spots,
Dark-spotted Leopard,
Fierce old man Leopard,
Even when his teeth are gone, he kills his prey with
    his head!

                                                          Sotho

THE BLESSING

The chase was swift
and the end came fast
the confrontation
of predator and victim.
The leopard
quivering with intent
tail swishing
eyes staring
blank
with the query of hunger ...

154

the baboon
terrified at first
of the mysterious query
to which he has no answer
turns
yields
to the merciful kiss
a strange consent
between them
a blessing.

Bruce Hewett

YELLOW EYES

Blended by fading moonlight with the grass —
   The long brown grass that bends beneath the dew —
Supple, subtle, and silent: eyes of brass
   That rove in solemn fierceness o'er the view;
Seeking his living by the shadow'd walks
Of sleeping man: Ingwi the Leopard stalks.

Thing from the utter silence of the wild —
   Thing from the outer darkness of the night —
Father of terror, of grey fear the child,
Ingwi (in peace softer than silk; in fight
Harder than steel) cringing in fear draws nigh
To stay his hunger where the White Men lie.

The chickens huddle in an abject dread —
   A dread no more than he, the Hunter, knows,
Yet quenches and goes in to seek his bread
   Within the precincts of the wired close.
Goes in … and sudden finds that he has bought
His life to lose his life — that he is caught.

The weighted door has closed, and he is trapp'd …
   Gods of the Wilderness, what agony!
Dumbly he noses where the wires mapp'd
   Against the darkness show where all is free.
Dumbly he strives to stretch a fore-paw through
To touch the long grass, bending with the dew.

155

Dumbly he yearns toward the outer black
    (His moon, that has sunk down for ever now,)
He sees a rabbit loping down the track,
    And hears the chilly night-breeze lisp and sough,
Lisp in the leaves that were his but this day
And now seem leagues, and countless leagues, away.

Far, far away the brooding mountains lie,
    The silver streams that croon among the ferns,
The wide umsasas black against the sky,
    The dreaming valleys where the glow-worm burns.
The veld has vanish'd with the closing door —
The veld that shall be Ingwi's never more.

The flash of lights — the shouts of men awake!
    And like a thunderbolt he strikes the wire,
Struggling in fury for his life's own sake —
    Wrapp'd in a whirling madness of desire,
Gathering his mighty power in his rage,
With thrice-fold strength he tears away the cage.

He fights, and he is free; the door is down;
    The great dogs are upon him in a breath —
Great hunters — but the half-bred boar-hound brown
    Falls struggling in the sobbing throes of death;
And Flo, his mate, her neck ripp'd half away,
Sinks dead before this Fury brought to bay.

Gods of the Wilderness, Ingwi is free!
    The rabbit flies in ecstasy of fear,
And Ingwi seeks that place where he would be —
    Where neither man nor animal shall peer.
Coughing the choking life-blood as he goes,
He seeks a hidden death-bed that he knows.

Blended by coming dawn-light with the ground
    That drinks his crimson power as it drops;
Seeking his chosen hiding without sound,
    Though dry with suffering are his burning lips.
Silent and savage 'neath the paling sky,
Riddled with shot, Ingwi goes back to die.

Kingsley Fairbridge

A LEOPARD LIVES IN A MUU TREE

A leopard lives in a Muu tree
Watching my home.
My lambs are born speckled
My wives tie their skirts tight
And turn away -
Fearing mottled offspring.
They bathe when the moon is high
Soft and fecund
Splash cold mountain stream water on their nipples
Drop their skin skirts and call obscenities.
I'm besieged
I shall have to cut down the muu tree.
I'm besieged
I walk about stiff
Stroking my loins
A leopard lives outside my homestead
Watching my women
I have called him elder, the one-from-the-same-womb
He peers at me with slit eyes
His head held high
My sword has rusted in the scabbard.
My wives purse their lips
When owls call for mating
I'm besieged
They fetch cold mountain water
They crush the sugar cane
But refuse to touch my beer horn.
My fences are broken
My medicine bags torn
The hair on my loins is singed
The upright post at the gate has fallen /
My women are frisky
The leopard arches over my homestead
Eats my lambs
Resuscitating himself.

Jonathan Kariara

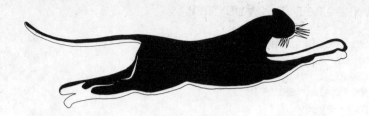

Ingw' idla ngamabala
The leopard eats by means of its spots.

It may be that the spots of the leopard serve as a camouflage, and enable it to take its victims unawares. Another explanation is that although the leopard is such a vicious animal, it is liked for its skin which is beautifully decorated. Its skin is preferred to that of other animals.

This proverb means that if one wants preference, he must have features which distinguish him from others. In a limited sense it means distinguishing oneself in the matter of dress. In a broader sense, it refers to achievements in life by the individual. These achievements are one's spots.

Zulu

Nkoe go lacoana di mebala.
Spotted leopards lick each other.
Birds of a feather flock together.

Sechuana

158

LION *Panthera leo*

NAMES
English: *Lion, King of the Beasts*
Afrikaans: *Leeu*
African: *ingonyama, ibhubesi (Z)*

DISTRIBUTION: Apart from a few hundred left in Asia, their distribution is today limited to Africa, between 12° N and 24° S. They prefer open savannah or open bush country.

DIET: Feeds mostly on hoofed animals such as zebra, giraffe or impala but will eat almost any animal they are able to overpower, even hyenas, cheetahs, locusts and termites. They will also eat carrion.

FEATURES AND HABITS: The mane of the male lion, which varies in colour from golden yellow through brown to almost black, distinguishes it from all other cats. Lions are essentially nocturnal but in areas where they are protected will show themselves fearlessly and even hunt during the day. In the heat of day they lie up in the shade of trees, long grass or thickets of bush and may spend as much as fifteen hours in twenty-four sleeping. When lions hunt in a pride they are more successful than when hunting on their own. The males usually drive the quarry towards the concealed and waiting females who do most of the killing. They are very quiet while the hunt is on but both sexes roar after a successful kill. The average number of lions found in a pride is normally between eight and twelve. Lionesses form the stable nucleus of a pride while the lions move from one pride to another quite regularly. Fights for possession of a pride and the right to mate are vicious. Displaced males may become nomadic loners or form small groups. Old or disabled lions as well as inexperienced young ones sometimes become man-eaters although this is not common. Man is the adult lion's only natural enemy. Lionesses normally conceive every two years and two to four cubs are born. They all have spots. More than half do not reach maturity because they are quite delicate, some are killed by predators such as hyena or by male lions, and some die of tick-borne diseases to which lions are particularly susceptible.

THE LION

The Lion, the Lion, he dwells in the waste,
He has a big head and a very small waist;
But his shoulders are stark, and his jaws are grim,
And a good little child will not play with him.

Hilaire Belloc

THE LIONESS AND THE CHILDREN

A Lioness was she who had
no children of her own.
She brought the people's children to
her place and cared for them.

She loved the children, for she felt
that they were born to her:
their mother was the lioness,
the people's children felt.

The lioness went down to drink.
While she was at the pool
a man, who saw that she had gone,
went to her place to speak.

He, speaking, told the children that
young lions they were not,
that they were people's children, who
should rise and walk back home.

'The bright fires of your people burn
on top of yonder hill,
roast flesh and honey are,' he said,
'where your own people dwell.'

The children, hearing this, arose.
They walked, they went away.
They went back to their people's place.
Also, the man went home.

The lioness, returning, saw
that her young ones had gone.
She stammered as she growled with rage:
"My children, where are they?"

She saw them walking on the hill
where there were many men.
She felt the men would kill her, if
she went to fetch them back.

Therefore she growled: "Chabbabbabbu"
for she felt that she would
kill people when she found them while
they walked when they were few.

Arthur Markowitz

LION AND SUN

When the parched
dusts of Africa
sting the nostrils
and the grasses
are as dry as
everlasting flowers
and the elephant
is a bulwark
of friendly advice
under the old thorn tree
comes the lion
swelling with pride
then comes the voice
of Africa's wilds
"Who is king of our day?"
and the lion
eye to eye with
the lionizing sun
answers boldly
while herds of buck run
"I am, I am, I am!"

Bruce Hewett

THE LION

Oh, weep for Mr, and Mrs. Bryan!
He was eaten by a lion;
Following which, the lion's lioness
Up and swallowed Bryan's Bryaness.

Ogden Nash

THE LION AND GIRAFFE

Wouldst thou view the Lion's den?
Search afar from haunts of men —
Where the reed-encircled rill
Oozes from the rocky hill,
By its verdure far descried
'Mid the desert brown and wide.

Close beside the sedgy brim
Couchant lurks the lion grim;
Watching till the close of day
Brings the death-devoted prey.
Heedless, at the ambushed brink
The tall Giraffe stoops down to drink:
Upon him straight the savage springs
With cruel joy. The desert rings
With clanging sound of desperate strife —
The prey is strong and he strives for life.
Plunging oft with frantic bound,
To shake the tyrant to the ground,
He shrieks — he rushes through the waste,
With glaring eye and headlong haste:
In vain! — the spoiler on his prize
Rides proudly — tearing as he flies.

For life — the victim's utmost speed
Is mustered in this hour of need:
For life — for life — his giant might
He strains, and pours his soul in flight;
And, mad with terror, thirst, and pain,
Spurns with wild hoof the thundering plain.

'Tis vain; the thirsty sands are drinking
His streaming blood — his strength is sinking;
The victor's fangs are in his veins —
His flanks are streaked with sanguine stains —
His panting breast in foam and gore
Is bathed — he reels — his race is o'er:
He falls — and, with convulsive throe,
Resigns his throat to the ravening foe!

Thomas Pringle

163

BIRDS

The lion, even when full of mud, with burrs
On his belly tangled, his great pads heavy
And cracked, sends such a message on the dry air
As makes all smaller animals wary, their fur
Rising in silken shivers, their horned heads
Up with the wind, reading its tragic story.

There is nothing majestic about death. Yet the king
Remains royal, and knows it; is accepted,
Though fled. Only the tiniest things —
The birds, whirr down from the tall sky, fling
Their feathered softnesses at shadows, dare to move
In his company, dare to sing.

Suppose a million birds could once shake loose
From the tops of trees, from the white horizon,
Veering in a soft outflinging noose,
Clouds in their clouds, lightning in their claws —
To peck out his sagging heart. How royally they would bedizen
His beggarman bones with the charity of their wings.

Ruth Miller

ANATOMY OF A LION

From out of the sabre thicket they took him,
Gnashing his sides with the thrusting thorn;
Huntsman who strayed into scanty forests,
Slayer of mewling calves to keep his engine fed;
Struck down as if by the searching light--
As the prancing ants that lap around a sugar cup
Ubiquitous, the earth destroys its hunger-driven sons.

And now, as if for manicure they lift paw by paw
To strip him of his proud crest,
Strip him of his hide that girdles the dark, sidereal
Spaces of his stomach and heart.

164

The viscera spill out blinking at the light,
The knuckle-bones wink —
A shadow of a lion, yet more real;
In outward things a phantasy, a dragon cloud
Drifting over the mopani at even —

Yet these organs spilled from the cavern
Tell us why, make me feel why
It was only slight misdirection that made
The necromancer prophesy from the viscera of a cock.

There are times when I feel cold from too much vision.
It does not help at times to know the reasons for our drives
                                                    and ecstasies;
Push back the sacs and tubes,
Strengthen and restore the bone,
Give him his shaggy hair and jacket again
So that my dreams, as much as he,
Can wander the miles of water, grass and trees under the moon
Securely feeling the spirit
Expectant and drawn tight as a silver bow.

                                                    Colin Style

Shumba hairairi chipashupashu.
A lion does not sup on grasshoppers.
Rich people do not depend on small things.

                                                    Shona

Tau erile 'ke motho ke le nosi.'
Engoe eare ke 'motho ka ba bangoe.'
The lion said 'Alone I am a man'; The other said 'By the aid of others I
am a man.'
Show me the man who would go to heaven alone, and I will show you one
who will never be admitted.

                                                    Sechuana

L

LIZARD *Class Reptilia, Order Squamata* (to which snakes also belong), Sub-order Sauria. There are 21 families of lizards in the world constituting about 3 000 known species. Some 300 species, representing 9 families, are found in South Africa.

NAMES
English: *Lizard: depending on the family referred to; gecko, leguan, sun-gazer, agama etc. With further variations depending on the species such as Nile monitor for a water leguan.*
Afrikaans: *Akkedis: nagakkedis, likkewaan, ouvolk, koggelmannetjie etc.*
African: *uhlobo lewentulo encane, isibankwa, uxamu (Z)*

DISTRIBUTION: Widely distributed throughout all temperate and tropical regions. They are found on coastal plains and high mountains, in forests as well as deserts. They live on the ground, in the sand, on rocks and in trees or water.

DIET: Most are insectivorous, some also eat plant material and others, such as the leguans, are carnivorous and will also eat eggs, carrion, etc.

FEATURES AND HABITS: Lizards display a great variety of shapes, sizes and habits and are marvellously adapted to their environment. Leguans are the largest African lizards. The largest lizard in the world, the 'Komodo dragon' is a member of the same family. Although there are lizards - some skinks for example - that are completely without legs, most have well developed, five-toed limbs. This is one of the more obvious differences between them and snakes. Their toes may be provided with - claws to fascilitate running on rock surfaces; webbing to walk on sand with greater ease; adhesive pads for climbing walls; or be adapted for tree climbing as in the case of chameleons. There are diurnal as well as nocturnal lizards. Their bodies are covered with scales and characteristic patterning. Some lizards are capable óf camouflage by changing colour. They are preyed upon by snakes, birds, cats, etc. and most have the ability to shed their tails to divert attention while making a getaway. In Central Africa the leguan's meat is highly prized for eating while in South Africa parts of its body are supposed to have medicinal value. In spite of the fact that all lizards, except two species in North America, are non-poisonous, many people fear them or are superstitious about them. Most lizards are oviparous, some are ovoviviparous and, in a few exceptional cases, viviparous.

THE SOUND OF SILENCE

I saw the sealed lips
of ancient walls
And though I asked
    Who lived here
    Who peered through that window
    to watch the gathering storm
    or the gentle evening
    congealing to darkness
    or morning
    melting to smiling skies

Who cooked in that hearth
now sewn together
in a shroud of jungle grass
I heard not a word

I saw gashes
time-inflicted
time-healed
on the half-demolished stone-walls

and the lizard
hated the messenger of death
glid-wriggled
flashing for one moment
before disappearing
into the stony silence

Then, looking at the silence
I knew the answer.

Daniel P Kunene

LIZARD

Drawing stillnes from the stone
Lizard joins quickness
To unmoving rock.
Stone breathes.
Blind mountain sees.
Noon's emptiness is filled.

Alert in time's crevice
The still creature is flexed stone,
Is breathing rock,
Is pulse below
The stretched blue skin of sky.
Under sun's weight
Aliveness is.

Wind flares.
The bright ground lifts up dust.
Light shines on life
And mountain rises up.

Anne Yates

Hapanawo chisingadi ushe gwavava ndiye nhevanji woruware.
There is none who does not want chieftanship, the lizard is first-born
of the rock.

Status is attractive to most people.

Shona

Go Naga-di-bogale go loeloa moruti le kgantlape.
In 'fertile lands' folks do nothing all the day long but fight with lizards for
the best places in the shade.

Lubberland! Where they have half a crown a day for sleeping,
Where the pigs run about ready roasted and cry 'Come, eat me!'

Sechuana

M

MANTIS Order *Orthoptera* : species *Mantidae,* of which more than 600 have been described.

NAME
English: *Praying - or sometimes Preying Mantis*
Afrikaans: *Hotnotsgot, Hottentotsgot*
African: *isithwalambiza (Z)*

DISTRIBUTION: All over the world except in the polar regions.

DIET: Insectivorous.

FEATURES AND HABITS: Mantids are predacious, and in this they differ from other members of the same order, such as crickets and grass hoppers. The females especially, are cannibals and have the habit of eating the males after being fertilised by them. The mantis stalks its prey by moving very slowly, in a series of jerks and then striking out with its frong legs. Some of the most amazing examples of camouflage in the animal kingdom are found amongst the mantids. They are variously adapted to resemble twigs, leaves, flower petals, etc. Most, but not all mantids are strong fliers. Eggs are layed in a whitish capsule made of a special glandular secretion. Mantids usually winter in the egg stage and there is one generation a year. Newly hatched nymphs look like the adults except that they are small and black. They undergo a series of moults as they grow.

The Mantis is the subject of many and confusing stories. Because of his characteristic posture, in which the front portion of his body is held erect and his front legs lifted in a supplicating gesture, he is frequently called the Praying Mantis. The docile-looking arms, however, are held in readiness to extend their spikes and hooks with lightning speed to seize unwary insects for prey. He is a deadly little predator, and should be called the Preying Mantis.

He is sometimes called the Hottentot God. It is possible, however, that neither the Hottentots (Khoi) nor the Bushmen (San) ever worshipped this insect, although they have stories about him. The error seems to have come from a misinterpretation of his name. It has been suggested by Martin Gusinde that the name of the Bushman god Kaggen can very easily be confused with their name for the praying mantis - an error made, it seems, by the German traveller Kolben in the eighteenth century who was 'most responsible for the myth among European settlers that the mantis was actually the god of the Hottentots.' (See A.C. Partridge *Folklore of Southern Africa*, Cape Town, Purnell, 1975 qv.) No representation of the Mantis has been found in rock art.

MANTIS

Green as an early leaf in Spring
He was, and no less green for being
Caught green-handed on an Autumn day
When puckered browns were everywhere.
My looming shadow held him there
In such a zone of worry as may
Make the least inclined to prayer
Suddenly inclined to pray.
It is improbable of course
That he could take the longer view
Beyond my local whelm of force
And pray in aid some primal Cause
Of whose effects we two were two;
Yet demonstrably there he was,
Clasping each green hand in each —
First in my shadow withdrew,
As if in such thanksgiving mood
As those least given to gratitude
Are not entirely stranger to.

Robert Dederick

MANTIS

He lifts his small hands
To god of nothingness.
Jagged legs stand
On pale green crutches.
The pear-shaped pod
Flanged for flight
All dainty lines
Except the Head:
Except the triangle terrible as death.

Responding to his hands, I touched him once.
His minute mouth roared
In such a horror of silence that I saw;
I saw his face grow large as mine
The tender spring green blade of him

Thrust like vengeance. His vicious eyes
Glared. His mouth was red
As hell, the pointed face
Filling with knowledgeable malice.
His hands —
Came for me, crept for me, felt for me through the space
Of cosmic distances that make an inch.

Now that I am brittle as a twig
Time having squeezed the sap and wrung me dry
To the bone, to the outdistancing brain,
Being careful to be quiet and restrained,
Would the terrible triangle of my face
Make him afraid?

Ruth Miller

M

MONKEY Like baboons, monkeys are primates of the suborder *Anthropiodea* of the Family *Cercopithecidae*. This family includes approximately sixteen *genera* and numerous species. African monkeys belong to either the *guenon* or the *guereza* group. The *guenon* are tree-dwellers and have cheek pouches for temporary food storage. The *guereza* do not have cheek pouches, they lack thumbs and have striking manes of long hair, usually black and white or combinations of rufous, bay, or chestnut.

NAMES
English: *Monkey; Vervet-, Samango-, Diana-, etc., depending on the species referred to.*
Afrikaans: *Aap; Blou-, Samango-, etc.*
African: *inkawu; insimango (Z)*
Scientific: *according to species e.g.: Vervet - Cercopithecus pygerythrus, Samango - Cercopithecus albogularis.*

DISTRIBUTION: Typical members of the *guenon* group are: Vervets, common in savannah woodlands and riverine areas, from the south-western Cape, north to southern Ethiopia; and samangos, found along the eastern side of the continent up to Kenya. Typical members of the *guereza* group are the Colobus species and they are inhabitants of the tropical forests of Africa.

DIET : *Guereza* monkeys are exclusively vegetarian. *Guenons* have a more varied diet of fruit, seed, insects, bird's eggs and grains.

FEATURES AND HABITS: Most monkeys have a thin hair covering over most of their bodies but the faces, as well as the hands and feet, are naked. Most species have 'sitting pads' or callosities on the buttocks. They have the same number of teeth as man, i.e. 32. Although some members of the *Cercopithecidae* family, such as the baboons, are more terrestial of habit most species are largely arboreal. Monkeys are gregarious animals and may be found in groups of as few as four or as many as a hundred or more members. Within the groups the habits and social structure vary, depending on the species. There is usually a definite 'pecking order' or hierarchy amongst the males in a group. Caring for and teaching the young are duties almost exclusively undertaken by the females who have very strong maternal instincts. One baby (sometimes two) is born after a gestation of roughly six months. Predators such as leopards and larger birds of prey are their chief enemies. They are also often killed by man because they cause crop damage, and in the past their skins were much sought after.

PRIMATES

Festooned upon the seedpod tree, like furry fruit,
Monkeys seem to bite their nails, the oft
Cracking and dropping of fine debris instils
A meditative air into the scene.
One uncoils and lopes down a limb, others aloft
Thrash and tumble down - the tree springs and reels.
It dandles them and they amble out of its arms.
They were eating pods. Now they've spotted our meal.

And so it comes about, this absurd situation,
That lower primates squat around and flick
Their small black eyes at our laden table.

So we too look anew at this spread of food
And think of how all day they must sift and pick
Over the ground to spy out seeds, tiny fruit, specks
Of edible stuff. They never feast. It would be crude
To throw a crust: manna from higher primates.

Original itinerants! Tinkers, men of wit:
They're free of Mondays, no one tells them off.
Their lives have grown no larger than their fur.
A life in the high trees! Their only leisured sway
That of wind in the leaves, and the daily drift
Over the kopjes. As for me, I sit
Framed in forms and structures, well-insured
Against my fears. But they are free, and they are prey.

Homo Erectus demonstrates his feat
With forepaw gestures brought to the display.
They leap among the rocks, their passage fades.
We contemplate our spread, then we eat.
Later, the car loaded and we ready to go,
We pause, caught by the soft rustle of the glades,
And boulder silence - all the depths beyond:
It folds down and lies there, under everything we do.

Rowland Molony

Inkaw' isina nesikhweb' etsheni
The monkey dances with a cob on a stone. At the first sign of danger
a monkey will flee; but instead of making a clean getaway, he will
pause to look back, holding the evidence of his crime. One should not
rejoice too soon, but should wait until one is out of danger.

Zulu

A u ruta choene mapalamo?
Are you teaching a monkey the way to climb?
Don't teach fishes to swim.

Choene ga ipone mariba.
A monkey doesn't see its own hollow eyes.
The eye that sees all things else, sees not itself.

Sechuana

N

NAGAPIE Two species of bushbabies or galagos occur in southern Africa. The Lesser Bushbaby is the smallest by far, and the other is known as a Nagapie.

NAMES
English: *Lesser Bushbaby, Nagapie*
Afrikaans: *Nagapie*
African: *isinkwe(Z)*
Scientific: *Galago senegalensis*

DISTRIBUTION: Savannah bushveld of southern Africa, especially where there are many acacia thorn trees.

DIET: They eat gum exuded by many trees such as the acacia, berries, fruit, seed and insects.

FEATURES AND HABITS: Nagapies are squirrel-like creatures with enormous ears and eyes. The eyes are fixed in their sockets and for this reason the little head is moved about continually as it looks around. They are strictly arboreal and nocturnal. During the day they sleep in family parties of two to seven, tightly curled up in tree hollows, tangled creepers or platform-like nests constructed of leaves and grass high up in trees. They have a distinctive range of sounds which vary between high-pitched chirping, chattering and a plaintive sob. They have clearly demarcated territories and the males will sometimes fight quite viciously. They grapple and bite but also use their forepaws a lot, looking for all the world like miniature boxers. Their main enemies are genets and owls. One or two babies are born in the nest or hole during summer. Nagapies are frequently captured by man, and illegally kept as pets.

NAGAPIE (BUSHBABY)

Night lent me his eyes. Now
I sit on his shoulder and stare
and stare I must from two
yellow eyes, close set
for better sight.

Night's my cage in which I gaily
hop from box to grate and back
small, deft, equipped
with hand-like feet, merely
to clamber more surely.

Bushbaby in night's warm jacket
between whose lapels I peep
out at the great performance,
don't squeak, don't bite, sit mum,
like one who's dumb.

Ape is my name, that's half of me,
not much at night and almost nothing
by day. Come on, grab me by my tail,
stuff me in a sack, and I'll still look
to see how you look.

Coo and chuckle at my capers,
leaping I still am me, abducted
still me, caged still me, always
me, staring I remain
envoy from night's domain.

Wilma Stockenström
Trans. Guy Butler

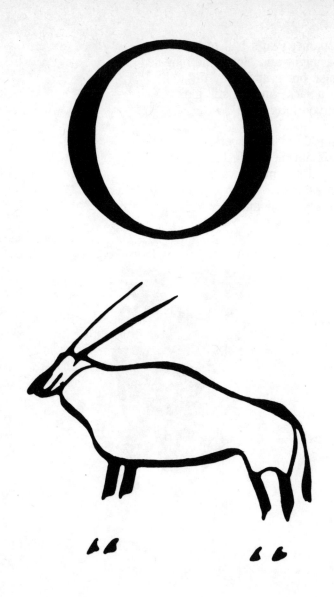

ORYX *Oryx gasella*

NAMES
English: *Gemsbok, Oryx.*
Afrikaans: *Gemsbok*
African: *inyamazane enezimpodo ezinde ezithe thwi zase zibheka emuva*

DISTRIBUTION: Arid areas such as the Kalahari Gemsbok park and Namibia in southern Africa; also three to four subspecies further north on the continent.

DIET: They are grazers but will browse if they have to. During very dry periods they dig out tsama melons, succulent roots and bulbs which have a high water content. They drink regularly if water is available but can go without for long periods.

FEATURES AND HABITS: One of the most handsome antelopes with rapier-like horns, black and white face patterns, flowing dark brown tail and dramatically marked greyish-fawn body. The gemsbok is a coveted hunting trophy but because its natural habitat is hostile to man this is not too serious a threat. It is extremely well adapted to life in a hot and dry environment: the underbelly is white and absorbs very little of the heat reflected off the desert sand; moisture is conserved by not having to sweat — its body temperature is allowed to rise and only the blood supply to the brain is cooled by circulating through a network of special vessels in the nose; ultra-efficient kidneys concentrate the urine to a few drops to conserve water. Under normal circumstances gemsbok form small, mixed herds of 10 - 30 animals under a dominant male. Territorial interlopers are warned off and vicious fights between dominant males are quite common. They are very shy antelopes but become pugnacious when wounded or cornered. When threatened by a lion or hyena, its main enemies apart from man, it will protect its rear by backing into a thorn bush and defend itself for hours by sweeping and thrusting with the lethal horns. After a gestation of 9 months, one calf is born. The mother and calf rejoin the herd only after about three to six weeks.

KALAHARI ORYX

Out of this ragged land burnt by sun and wind,
Cut by canyons dust powdered and golden,
Out of the masterful silences,
Out of the locked cloud taverns.
Out of this land
You loom flame-like on a browed dune
In statued beauty.
And in the sheltered valleys of your copper country
Out of the brass wind and silica sun,
After the furnace,

In the low afternoons
You herd together and listen
While the night agony of the lion shakes the desert.
For the lion knows your wind speed and horn danger,
Hunts carefully and dreams of your beauty
In the sun.
When the ice night falls
And purple stars flicker in diamond hard silences
You sleep fitfully on a gentle knee
Hearing the darkness,
Hearing the rustling of black silk
Which is like a moving of small animals
While out of a mauve infinity
Out of the cold sky
A dew falls light as air
Upon the grand unchartered vistas of your home.
The night is danger swift
And in the dawn of colour-wide confusion
You stir in your pastel shadows
To stand upon a moulded hill as pale as death
And test the air.
Your horns are swords that cut the sky,
Your bone-black hooves are poised for flight,
You are a hide of light,
An eagle of an eye.
You are the proud perfected art,
The love of all this dreaming land.

Hjalmar Thesen

... 'Heisib had a gemsbok wife (Thomas, 1950) in addition to his
natural wife. He paid special attention to his gemsbok wife - to the
extent that his natural wife and sons felt neglected and went to find
the rival for Heisib's affections. They discovered her "there in the
plain, sitting in plenty, eating meat and honey". Heisib's natural wife
then slew the gemsbok wife "knowing well that meat is not a wife"
and Heisib's mother decreed: "hereafter shall meat be meat and men
shall be men. Hereafter those finding gemsbok in the plains shall hunt
and slay them, for they are food to be eaten of men.'

Woodhouse

O

OSTRICH Family *Struthionidae* which has three other members - *rhea, emu* and *cassowary*.

NAMES
English: *Ostrich*
Afrikaans: *Volstruis*
African: *intshe (Z)*
Scientific: *Struthio camelus*

DISTRIBUTION: Drier parts of Africa, Syria and Arabia.

DIET: Plants, berries and seeds. Hard objects such as pebbles are swallowed to assist digestion.

FEATURES AND HABITS: The ostrich is the largest living bird. It cannot fly but has powerful legs and can escape an enemy by running at a maximum speed of about 70km per hour. It will also defend itself by kicking. Its beautiful plumage is unique - feathers of other members of the family are valueless. Unlike most birds, the feathers are not oiled and so they do not repel water. There is no truth in the popular legend that an ostrich hides its head in the sand in the face of danger. They are usually found in small parties but often singly. The male utters a dull roar, especially at night. They are normally monogamous but up to three females may accompany a single male and lay in the same nest. The nest is a mere scrape in the ground and contains 15 - 20 eggs. The conspicuous black and white male usually sits on the eggs at night while the drab female sits by day when her colouring blends in well with the surrounding veld.

In South Africa commercial ostrich farming began in about 1860 and, to a greater or lesser extent, has been going on ever since. Wing feathers and leather are in demand as fashion accesories; other feathers are used for making feather-dusters; the meat is used fresh, or dried as biltong; the eggs, which have the same volume as about two dozen hens eggs, make good eating and are also sold as souvenirs; even the bones are used for bone-meal. The feathers are plucked every 8 - 10 months and the process is absolutely painless.

THE OSTRICH

The ostrich roams the great Sahara.
Its mouth is wide, its neck is narra.
It has such long and lofty legs,
I'm glad it sits to lay its eggs.

Ogden Nash

OSTRICH

Here again the scaly legs and frightful
Toenails of the aged aunt I never could
Stomach. Thick knees, elevated bust
And that arse-disdainful walk; she balding
Too, a fuzz of prickles all that's left
On the old pate; mouth wide enough
To swallow saucers. Never never could you
Among chips in breadcrumbed segments be
Fingerlickingood. And yet on wingtips
(What evolutionary cul-de-sac are you
Haughtily lost in, Lady Windermere?) and
On tail, there, surely, is something
Victorian and gracious: a suggestion of
The must and gloom of drapes in drawing-
Rooms, a tasselled bell-rope, the heavy
Woody formalities in bustles that could
So easily mask hilarious scaly legs.

Rowland Molony

Bonche ga ba tlhakanele kutta.
Ostriches never share the same nest.

Two women in one house,
Two cats and one mouse,
Two dogs and one bone,
Never will accord in one.

Sechuana

185

P

PORCUPINE There are two families of porcupines: *Hystricidae* (Old World porcupines) and *Erethizontidae* (New World porcupines).

NAMES
English:	*Porcupine: Cape or South African*
Afrikaans:	*Ystervark*
African:	*ingungumbane (Z), noko (N-S)*
Scientific:	*Hystrix africaeaustralis;* the Old World porcupine of southern Africa belongs to a subfamily *Hystricinae* (true porcupines). The other subfamily is *Atherurinae* (brush-tailed porcupines).

186

DISTRIBUTION: Old World porcupines are found all over Africa, southern Europe and southern Asia, in almost every type of country, flat to hilly, open to forested.

DIET: Bulbs and roots, fruits, the bark of certain trees and vegetable matter in general. It is a wasteful feeder and does much damage to cultivated crops.

FEATURES AND HABITS: *Hystrix africaeaustralis* is the largest rodent in Africa. It is easily recognised by black and white ringed quills which cover its back and tail, and a bristly crest on its head. The black (or dark brown) and white colour theme is prevalent among all porcupines although there are a few exceptions in the New World – one North American porcupine has black-tipped, yellow quills. The hollow, open-ended tail-quills make a surprisingly loud, rattling noise. The quills are loosely attached and fly in all directions when the animal shakes himself violently. This has given rise to the erroneous belief that porcupines 'fire' their quills at enemies. Quills do get lodged in the flesh of attackers and as this causes suppurating wounds and even death it is easy to understand why predators tend to avoid them. Porcupines are nocturnal and spend the day in deep burrows. They live in groups of three to four animals but forage alone at night. One to four young are born after a gestation of seven weeks. The babies remain in the burrow until their quills have grown and hardened. Porcupines make very good eating according to some people but they are not easily trapped, being very cautious and intelligent.

THE PORCUPINE

What! would you slap the Porcupine?
    Unhappy child – desist!
Alas! that any friend of mine
    Should turn Tupto-philist.

To strike the meanest and the least
    Of creatures is a sin,
How much more bad to beat a beast
    With prickles on its skin.

Hilaire Belloc

THE HUNTING OF THE PORCUPINE

When lying in wait for a porcupine,
I must not sleep.
I must watch when the porcupine draws near,
I must stay awake,
for he is the one who wants us to sleep
against our will
that we may not see him when he comes back
to hide in his hole.

Therefore, if we sleep, he steals softly by.
(He lifts his quills
that they may not rattle and wake us up
before he has gone.)
Because he does this, I must stay awake,
for if I slept,
he should come and go and I should think that
he had not yet come.

Therefore, when I wait for the porcupine,
I keep awake.
I do not sleep when I wait for him to
come back in the dark.
The porcupine he is not one who goes
about at noon,
for he cannot see when the sun is bright
and dazzles his eyes.

Night is the time when the porcupine's eyes
see all things well,
while his nostrils are those which tell him if
there is to be peace.
When the porcupine comes, I touch the breeze,
I must take care
while he is not one who, returning, walks
right out of the wind.

He crosses the wind in a slanting way,
he sniffs to smell,
for his nostrils are those which tell him if
there is harm about.

188

I must not sleep, therefore, or move my limbs,
I must keep still,
away from the wind that carries my scent
and tells where I am.

Also, I must not breathe loudly while
I lie in wait,
for the porcupine is a thing which does
perceive every sound.
His ears hear finely, I must make no noise
or break a twig,
for the rustle would make the porcupine
hear me and turn back.

Arthur Markowitz

ONE THAT WAS NEVER SEEN

One that was never seen
the golden porcupine
running in the long dawn
grass near the tent
of Cleopatra
raised his spine
and bit through the long
fresh vineleaves
with a subtle tooth.

Sydney Clouts

As it is normally nocturnal, the Bushmen credit the porcupine with the
ability to tell the time by the stars so that it knows of the approach of
dawn and can retreat to its lair. In this it was said to be accompanied
by bats (Bleek, 1912, p.247) and to exercise the power of making men
sleepy so that they would not lie in wait for it. If anyone was able to
overcome this sleepiness he had to keep very quiet, because of the
acute hearing of the porcupine. He also had to take into account that it
would walk "across the wind" so as to catch any warning scent.

Woodhouse

189

P

PUFFADDER *Bitis arietans arietans*

NAMES
English: *Puffadder*
Afrikaans: *Pofadder*
African: *iBululu (Z,Xh,Nd), Lebolobolo (Tsw, N.S.) Vuluvulu (V), Chiva (Sh).*

DISTRIBUTION: Throughout Africa, extending into southern Arabia. Absent from forest areas and extreme deserts.

DIET: Small ground-living mammals such as rats and mice but will also take cold-blooded prey such as lizards and toads.

FEATURES AND HABITS: The puffadder has a heavy, fat body with a short stubby tail, longer in the male than in the female. In South Africa the average length is under one metre. The head is broad, flattened and subtriangular. Its colour varies from shades of yellow to orange-brown with dark-brown to black chevron-shaped bands over the back and tail. It is a very sluggish snake and depends on its camouflage to escape notice. For this reason it is also very dangerous because it is often trodden on by man and beast. When distrubed it inflates itself with air which it lets out again with a loud 'puff' as a warning that it is about to strike. It is most active at night when it goes in search of food. Warm-blooded prey is first killed with its poison and then swallowed, head first. Cold-blooded prey is swallowed live. They feed hugely in summer to store up fat which has to tide them over their winter hibernation. Like other members of the genus it is ovoviviparous, i.e. it produces its young 'live'. Depending on the size of the mother 20 to 150 young may be born, usually in summer or early autumn. Man is its chief enemy but birds of prey, mongooses and warthogs also prey on it. It is interesting to note that some animals, especially members of the pig family and also guinea-pigs, display a high resistance to puffadder venom. The venom is mainly haematoxic but possesses certain neurotoxic properties. It causes internal bleeding and is potentially deadly to man although death may occur only after 24 hours or more and in only 5% of cases. The puffadder is probably the most widespread and dangerous snake in South Africa and responsible for more stock deaths than any other snake.

THE PUFF-ADDER

Here where the grey rhenoster clothes the hill,
    Drowsing beside a boulder in the sun,
Slumbrous-inert, so gloomy and so still,
    On the warm steep where aimless sheep-paths run,
A short thick length of chevron-pattern'd skin,
    A wide flat head so lazy on the sand,
Unblinking eyes that warn of power within,
    Lies he, — the limbless terror of the land.

He is the ablest specialist in death, —
    This gleam of living velvet — and in this
He finds his pride; yet, with presaging breath,
    He warns the unwary footstep with a hiss.
Go, then, and live. Remain, and in a flash
    The fangs have found their victim, and the stark
Strong hand of death with instant awful lash
    Hath struck thee, choking, to the utter dark.

Sober and thoughtful, passionless he lies
    Dreaming strange dreams that are not ours to know,
While the sun wanders through unclouded skies,
    And insects, chirping round him, come and go;
Unmov'd, unvex'd by hatred or desire,
    Calm in resistless power he disdains
The fury-blinded rinkhals' insane ire,
    And rests impassive till the sunlight wanes.

Kingsley Fairbridge

LEVIATHAN

A puff-adder, khaki,
fatter than a stocking of pus
except for its short thin tail,
obese and quick
as certain light footed dancers
took a dozing lizard.

Scaly little monster
with delicate hands and feet
stupidly sluggish in the sun.
Panting, true,
but lizards breathe mostly
as if their lives depended.

Gone.
Enveloped by a slack
wormy yellow bowel.

O Jonah, to tumble to
those sickly, deadly depths,
slick walled, implacably black.

Douglas Livingstone

Puffadders store up large quantities of fat before winter, and for this
reason are much in demand by African herbalists, who dispense the fat
as a cure for rheumatism (V.F.M. FitzSimons, *Snakes of Southern
Africa,* p339.)

Thambo lenyoka hlab' omzondayo.
Bone of a snake, prick the one you hate.

This is a deadly threat. Snake bones are said to be dangerous, and
may result in death if they should prick one. The expression is used,
therefore, to an enemy that one would be happy to see dead.

Zulu

193

QUAGGA *Equus quagga*

NAMES

English: *Quagga*

Afrikaans: *Kwagga. Early pioneers and writers were not always very specific when talking or writing about animals. The names bergkwagga (mountain zebra) and bontkwagga (Burchell's zebra) were often shortened to just kwagga, causing some confusion today, when early documents are studied.*

African: *iQwara (Ngu) - today this word means striped or Zebra but originally it was probably used for the quagga.*

DISTRIBUTION: Extinct. Up to the middle of the nineteenth century they were found in the drier parts of the Cape Colony as well as the Orange Free State.

DIET: They were grazers like all other zebras, probably doing a bit of browsing under certain circumstances.

FEATURES AND HABITS: The true quagga had smallish ears and stripes only on its head, neck, shoulders and part of its trunk. It had a ground colour of dark rufous brown or bay, fading to white on the thighs and under-body, with white legs and tail and a dark stripe along its back. The quagga was once extremely common within its rather limited range. In 1840 Sir Cornwallis Harris wrote that their numbers had been greatly reduced but that south of the Vaal River there were 'interminable herds. Moving slowly across the ---- horizon, uttering a shrill barking neigh, of which its name forms a correct imitation, long files of quaggas continually remind the early traveller of a rival caravan on its march.' The quagga shared this habit of walking in single file with the black wildebeest in the company of which it was often seen, being a gregarious animal. Nothing is known of their breeding habits but they probably produced one foal at a time, like other zebra.

Quagga hides and meat were much in demand and thousands were killed, being easy prey as verified by Lichtenstein, a German doctor who visited the Cape in 1803 - 'The quaggas even came among our cattle as they were grazing and fed quietly with them.' As far as anybody knows the last quagga in the wild was shot near Aberdeen in 1858. It had never been regarded as an endangered animal and the very last living specimen in the world died in an Amsterdam Zoo on 12 August 1883 without anybody realizing what had happened. Twenty-three years later, in 1886, the Cape Government passed legislation giving the quagga legal protection!

QUAGGA: OBITUARY

Perhaps the most beautiful of the horse family (with the exception of the Unicorn), the Quagga has disappeared. His departure is shrouded in mystery. As relaxation from the routine struggles of protecting and feeding themselves and their flocks, our pioneering grandfathers found some relief in taking pot shots at as many forms of life as they could draw a bead on. That was fun. Was it not also subduing the earth and taming it, as in *Genesis* I v 28? But our fathers went one better than their fathers, using telescopic sights to reduce the beasts' sporting chances still further.

None of them, however, would have set out, deliberately, to shoot the last surviving animal of any species. Such paralysis of imagination would afflict them only when confronted by members of rival human breeds, such as Abo's and Bushmen. The Quagga's departure must not therefore be laid at the door of *Homo Sapiens*.

But if not Man, who is to blame? Let us consider the theory of a fellow primatologist, Ezekiel von Sonnenschein. The Quagga was wiped out as a deliberate act of genocide by the Yahoos (see page 253) prolific primates who during the eighteenth century escaped from an island in the Indian Ocean where they had long lived in subjection to a noble breed of horses *Equus Rationalis*. According to Sonnenschein, the Yahoos bore, deep in the race memory, recollections of their subjection to *Equus Rationalis*; so that, once they had acquired lethal weapons from *Homo Sapiens*, they took their revenge. Now, they could subdue and own horses, ride triumphant on the backs of horses, whip horses and dig spurs into them. Horses, however, were too useful to kill; but all other living reminders of their ancient subjection to the equine species were intolerable. All the horses' cousins must die.

Sonnenschein then gives some account of the Yahoo's bungled revenge. Zebras to date have proved too numerous and fleet to exterminate. Yahoo eyesight was so poor they could not even see Unicorns. The Mountain Zebra was easier meat; his difficult habitat however saved a remnant; but the Quagga, who had lost most of its stripes and accommodated itself to the yellow and gold of the highveld grasses; the Quagga, most docile of creatures; the Quagga, so opposite to all things Yahoo; the Quagga succumbed. Thus Sonnenschein.

However the polemic goes, the disappearance of the Quagga does coincide with the expansion into the interior of higher primates, whether Yahoo or *Homo Sapiens*, equipped with that symbol of high technology, the rifle.

Guy Butler

R

RHINOCEROS Family *Rhinocerotidae* - Five species extant in the world today, of which two are found in Africa and three in the Orient.

NAMES
English: *White or square-lipped rhinoceros*
          Black or hook-lipped rhinoceros
Afrikaans: *Witrenoster; Swartrenoster*
African: *umkhombe (white), ubhejane (black)-(Z)*
Scientific: *Ceratotherium simum - white*
          Diceros bicornis - black

197

DISTRIBUTION: Formerly white and black rhinos were fairly numerous and widespread, the black more so than the white. In southern Africa today both kinds are found in Natal and have also been reintroduced into areas of their former range such as the Kruger Park. The continued existence of rhinoceros populations north of the Limpopo River, especially. in East and Central Africa, are at risk. An alarming number of animals are illegally killed for their horns which are used as aphrodisiac, for medicinal purposes and for making traditional Arab dagger handles.

DIET: The white rhino is a grazer and eats mostly grass while the black rhino is a browser, eating leaves and shoots, but also some grass. Both kinds use their mobile lips for plucking their food.

FEATURES AND HABITS: The rhinoceros is a huge three-toed mammal. The names 'white' and 'black' rhino are misnomers. Both kinds are grey and take on the colour of the local soil, being partial to mud-baths which help rid them of parasites such as ticks. The white or square-lipped rhino is larger and carries its head lower than the black or hook-lipped rhino. They have two horns (the black occasionally three). In the white rhino the rear horn is often the same length or longer than the front horn. The 'horns' are not true horn but compacted keratinous fibres, similar to hair, and attached to the skin rather than the skull. The white rhino is quite placid and normally found in groups of between four and eight animals. The black rhino is nervous, unpredictable, often aggressive and solitary. Rhinos avoid fights except when females are on heat. Violent confrontations between territorial males take place then, amid much noise. One calf is born to a cow in any season. They fall prey to predators such as lion and hyena quite often although the mother defends her calf vigorously. The white rhino mother normally follows close behind the calf while the black rhino calf always follows the mother.

RHINOCEROS

The rhino is a homely beast
For human eyes, he's not a feast.
Farewell, farewell, you old rhinoceros,
I'll stare at something less prepoceros.

Ogden Nash

RHINOCEROS

Ants and birds trace patterns in the dirt, but these creatures,
Armageddon in their shoulders, slip out of sight,
Sun at the meridian, and we are afraid to move
During the interregnum of the afternoon
Lest we encounter their colossal shadows,
Centres of gravity that flatten the grass
And range with unimaginable violence
Over the countryside we have rashly entered.

It is a landscape from which men are absent,
But not because they have migrated to the towns.
The stumps and trunks of trees clutter our path, and in
    the odd clearing
Evidence remains of human habitation,
Thatching grass and roof-poles not altogether destroyed by fire.
In these villages they paused and then disappeared,
Swept up like shadows in the aftermath of the sun.

We do not mind where we go, provided we do not meet them,
The missing people who occupied the savannah.
Trespassing in their pillaged territory
We might find the rhinoceros, we might hear him
Stamping the earth to tears.

                                              Harold Farmer

ZEUS RHINOCEROS

She was walking with friends near Marseilles
when Olympian cloudlets
signalled far away
to the ripple-bearded
master of Olympus sagged in wrinkles,
virtually formless,
her lovely arms quite bare as were the ocean's

and
her lifeless eye
her witch-white face.

Europe desperately has tried to restore her spiritual
vigour after the failure of her churches to bring
salvation, of her philosophers to bring order, of her
policies to bring unity, to her members, through edicts,
indulgences, councils, dualisms, wars and economic
savagery.

She was walking with her friends near Marseilles
when seasniffing flowerchewing
cattle bulked by with amongst them one, one
so strange and grim as wrinkled iron, weak-
eyed, clumsy, but boding in his horn
the plains
the forests
of a light she had never known.

Irresistible farewell!
His bony back was heaven, then
his bony back was water, blue
Mediterranean.

Relinquishing her ancient coasts the lissom harlot loved
the spray, the immense island of that plunging god who
smiled bleakly without virtue, boasting through his
armour, bore her deep, then rolled so she was curled into
the long waves cut by a Moroccan vessel heading south;
and sang

In the hour of the laurel
in the snow-wind
in the sunwind,
born in the error
of a perfect song,
I kissed the laurel as I rose
I kiss the laurel now
in the ashes of the laurel,
of the fateful
seacrest
berries of the bush.

Sydney Clouts

Mukadzi akarambwa inhema yokumutsira.
A divorced woman is a rhino that has been roused, ie. powerful and
dangerous.

But when contextually opposed to the elephant, the rhino can be a
symbol of trifles.

Shona

SCORPION Class *Arachnida* Order *Scorpionida*. There are more than 600 species in the world of which about one quarter are found in southern Africa.

NAMES
English: *Scorpion*
Afrikaans: *Skerpioen*
African: *ufesela (Z), lesikisiki (N-S)*
Scientific: All scorpions found in southern Africa belong to one of two families; *Scorpionidae* and *Buthidae*.

DISTRIBUTION: They are found in tropical, sub-tropical and temperate parts of the world - in deserts, forests and tropical jungles - from sea-level to 5 000 metres above sea-level in the Andes mountains.

DIET: Entirely carnivorous.

FEATURES AND HABITS: Scorpions may be regarded as living fossils, being the most primitive of all land arachnids. This predacious creature has been feared by man since ancient times. The Greeks showed their respect for the scorpion by naming one of the constellations after it. Its most distinctive features are the pair of powerful claws at the head and the vesicle or 'sting' at the tail, which curves over the back in attack or defence. There is no truth in the story that scorpions sting themselves to death. The poison injected with the sting is potent and causes instant death in spiders, centipedes, etc. and great discomfort and sometimes death in humans. The prey is held by the pinching-claws or pedipalps and masticated by small chelicerae between the pedipalps. It lacks jaws and only the soft parts of a victim are absorbed in semi-liquid form. *Scorpionidae* and *Buthidae* are easily distinguished in that the former has a thin tail and strong claws whereas the latter has a thick, powerful tail and slender claws. The poison glands of the Buthidae are much larger and its poison more toxic. Scorpions are usually solitary except in the mating season when small colonies are found together. An elaborate courtship dance is performed by the two sexes before mating takes place. After mating the male is often killed by the female. Scorpions are ovoviviparous and between 20 and 40 young are born at the beginning of summer after a gestation of up to and sometimes more than a year. They are carried about on their mother's backs and undergo a series of moults before becoming independent.

THE SCORPION

The Scorpion is as black as soot,
    He dearly loves to bite;
He is a most unpleasant brute
    To find in bed, at night.

Hilaire Belloc

THE SCORPION

Limpopo and Tugela churned
In flood for brown and angry miles
Melons, maize, domestic thatch,
The trunks of trees and crocodiles;

The swollen estuaries were thick
With flotsam, in the sun one saw
The corpse of a young negress bruised
By rocks, and rolling on the shore,

Pushed by the waves of morning, rolled
Impersonally among shells,
With lolling breasts and bleeding eyes,
And round her neck were beads and bells.

That was the Africa we knew,
Where, wandering alone,
We saw, heraldic in the heat,
A scorpion on a stone.

William Plomer

A SHADE FOR SCORPIONS

When fire kisses fire, there you get
                              a shade for scorpions:

blunt stones baking in the sun,
in their sparse room red eyes alert
for a heat-dazed grub or worm, some
unwary tarantula they can pounce on
and drag it, the body still steaming, smoking ...

Not all are cut out for this biting frolic
                              this harsh amour.

Stripped in the light of this fever is one
who falls and fails, jerking upright again
to fall and fail again on peaked rocks

204

slanted like tables towards the surgical sun —
At length, being patient whom distemper shakes,
still unresigned, undisciplined to endure,
not curable suffers his detested cure:
outrageously aloof in deadly langour
he dies in tablelands whose shards conspire
like leeches, and sap him from his root of anger,
from the dry leaves, the stillness of his waiting
for a relief that lasts.

Perseus Adams

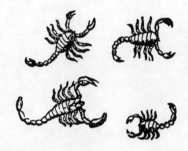

Kuzvizvarira kunge chinyavada.

To bring forth yourself (one like you) like a scorpion.

Children inherit the attributes of parents.

Shona

SNAKE Reptiles of the order *Squamata,* suborder *Serpentes.* There are about 3000 species and subspecies in the world, classified roughly into thirteen families.

NAMES
English: Snakes — specific names are used according to families or species
             adder (family); coral snake (species).
Afrikaans: *Slang; adder; koraalslang.*
African: *noga (N-S), inyoka (Z)*
Night-adder:*chiva (Sh), iNyoka yasebusuku (X)*
Coral-snake:*inKamela (X)*

DISTRIBUTION: Snakes are more widely distributed than their close relatives the lizards. They are adapted to a wide range of habitat; deserts and swamps, high mountains, the sea, rivers, trees and even underground. They are absent from Ireland, New Zealand, Bermuda, Hawaii, Azores and many isolated small islands.

DIET: Depending on the species, snakes live on birds, eggs, mammals, reptiles, other snakes, insects, snails, etc. Some are specialised feeders while others are more or less omnivorous.

FEATURES AND HABITS: Their most characteristic features are elongated bodies and a complete absence of limbs. This holds true for all species except the more primitive types such as pythons and boas which have vestigial hind limbs visible in the shape of small claw-like spurs. Snakes use one, or more, of four different techniques to move; lateral undulation of the body, sidewinding, caterpillar movement and a concertina type of movement. They are dry-skinned, smooth and cool to the touch. They shed their skins from time to time because these are made of a horny material which does not grow with the owner. First shedding takes place soon after birth and thereafter up to ten times a year under favourable growing conditions. They are sensitive to changes in temperature and avoid extremes – in summer by staying in the shade and in winter by going into hibernation. Snakes are not aggressive under normal circumstances and will try to get away as quickly as possible if disturbed. Most will, however, resort to some warning or protective measure when cornered – hissing, spreading a hood or shamming death are some examples. Less than one-third of all snakes are poisonous and these not all to the same degree. There are basically three types of venom: that of the *Elapids* (cobras, mambas, coral-snakes, etc) in which neurotoxic elements predominate; that of *Vipers* (night-adders, puff-adders, etc.) in which haematoxic elements predominate and where tissue destruction is caused; that of back-fanged snakes (tree-snake, vine-snake, etc.) which causes intravenous clotting of blood. Few snakes are wanderers and individuals usually stick to a particular small area or 'home range'. They are solitary creatures, except in the mating season or sometimes while hibernating. The belief that if you kill a snake its mate will come seeking revenge stems from the fact that during the mating season, which takes place just after hibernation or the first spring rains, snakes are often found in pairs, and if one is killed the other is bound to be seen in the same area. With the aid of its sensitive tongue a male is able to find a mate by picking up the scent left by glandular secretions of the latter. Quite an elaborate courtship takes place before mating. Most

snakes are oviparous and after the eggs are laid give them no further
attention. There are, however, exceptions — the female python incubates
her eggs by coiling herself round them. Some species are ovoviviparous
i.e. the eggs are retained in the female's body until fully incubated.
Depending on the species as few as three of four eggs, or as many as
100 or more may be laid. Today man is one of the snake's worst enemies.
Owing to an unreasoning fear of even the most harmless snakes, he kills
them without exception and takes no account of the important role these
creatures play in the control of rodents and other pests. Some people
regard snake-meat as a great delicacy and others make charms and
medicines from various parts of it's anatomy. There is also a great
demand for snake-skin leather and fancy goods and alarming numbers of
snakes, especially the big species such as pythons, are killed for this.
Apart from man, snakes have many enemies such as birds of prey, cats,
mongooses, leguans, other cannibalistic snakes, bullfrogs and natural
disasters like veld fires. Because of man's fear of snakes,
misconceptions, myths and superstitions about them abound. One of the
most common of these is that they hypnotize their prey — this is not
true but their fixed stare, resulting from the fact that they have no
eyelids, probably accounts for this belief. Cultures as diverse as the
Druids of ancient Britain, the Scandinavians, Egyptians, Chinese and
Incas have imbued snakes with supernatural powers of wisdom, fertility,
eternal youth, evil, etc.

THE REDEEMED

Woman with emerald swathed on your coppery flesh,
Yield, O yield like the rest,
Those orbs dancing
In the fold across your breast
Shall yield before your sun has set.

I am the snake that sucks
Sweet life out of eggs,
Yield she must yield.
In my eye is the curse
That must distress,
You must yield, O yield like the rest.

Love I the pillar of neck
Governing like a marvel the balance
Of load on your head
Yet must I break it -

Love I the shine of your skin
Yet must I dull it
With venom from my sting -

Love I the flaming melody of your frame
Yet must I silence it,
The ecstasy moving in your step
Yet must I make it burn out its fire
In me, a snake that must suck
Sweet life out of eggs,
I, that will not spare.
You smell of the woman Eve
And you must yield.

Come I then in the path you proudly walk,
Come I raging with madness of forest fire,
Come I, in the fever of my curse
Come I, to crush you,
Break the copper pillar of your neck,
Kill the mercury glint in you,
And leave you there
By the debris of your plantain load,
In the tangle of your emerald robe,
Spent, overcome.

She paused in her pace, and turned on me
A soul that speared my reptile frame
Until I writhed in a helpless coil
And the poison in me boiled
And clotted in the glare
From the splendour of her redeemed soul.

O woman swathed in emerald,
I am not able to be, as of old,
A cursed snake
And make you yield, O yield to me.

Her dark lips smiled,
Her dark eyes beamed delight,
The copper neck swerved back with its load,
And down the slope of the market road,
She strode.

Efua Sutherland

THE SNAKE AND THE LIZARD

A small commotion shivers the plant stems.
I part the leaves to find a lizard Mr. Michelin.
His eyes are closed as though in ecstasy:
Too deep in the suffusion of his blood,
Too sunk in the birth-and-death grin
To see the last of life outside his red world.
He looks pleased in the bursting of his brain.
Alas! He touched off the uncontrollable
Sprung rubber alarm clock: it bounced apart
All over him: boingg: it loves him to death.
The rubber loops contort, their moil and clench
Rockabyeing him out of this world.
The slow ease of mounting blood pressure
Pliant atoms grind together, the world is singing
(Overhead in the trees cicadas' electric
Pins-and-needles in the ears). Two grins here
At the end of all determination have set hard.
Such devoted wrestling; such giving
To the uttermost of bodies to this act!
I replace the flower heads, their coloured passions
Nodding for the death-throes at their roots.

Rowland Molony

THE SLITHERING MAMBA

The long snake is now on the metal spoor.
It is the metal snake that coughs and ejects smoke.
As if furious it growls and grunts like a pig.
It slithers along the metal spoor like a dog on the scent
While metal shafts continuously prod its jaws;
So the ground snake pants and puffs along.

It writhes along the valleys and in the bush.
This metal snake is carrying both the good and the bad
Who are comfortable sitting within its ribs.
Beautifully made houses follow each other.
Beast and man breathe freely in its belly.
The old and the young mingle freely in it.

When tired it rests for a while, panting all the time.
It spits out some people as it swallows others.
It resumes its journey, belching out smoke as dark as night,
And the sky chokes with it until it is pitch black.
The monster now works wonders on the veld.
It now heaves and huffs towards its destination.

Its eye is a spear which competes with the sun.
It gives light to those within.
On reaching its destination, it perspires heavily.
It opens its lungs to be refreshed by the breeze.
This is when it unloads countless people
Whose friends and relatives joyfully come to meet them.

The living, writhing snake has now reached its destination
Where it immediately cuts its head off
Like that of the legendary cockerel
Whose head left the body to go to the 'Shave' dance.
It will join the head at dawn.
This then is the slithering ground snake that refuses to live in a lair,
The long snake; the result of the white men's mischief.

Mordikai A. Hamutyinei

... the snakes were also men and their chief married a daughter of Cagn but Cagn sent his son Cogaz to bring her home. This angered the snakes who were away hunting and the young people of their tribe knew that on their return they would fill the country with water. As a precaution they built a platform of willow poles and took refuge on top of it with their chief. When their husbands returned after causing the flood, the female snakes threw them into the water where they drowned. Then Cagn struck the survivors with his stick and as he did so a person came out of each snake skin.

Bushman (Woodhouse)

Rangove zuru rakapinda nyoka.

It has become an anthill where a snake has entered.

i.e. A dangerous place.

Shona

Noga e itomile mogatla.
The snake has bitten its own tail.
The biter is sometimes bit.

Ba betsana ka noga e utloa.
They beat each other with a live snake.
They are at daggers drawn.

Sechuana

SPIDER Class *Arachnida* Order *Araneae*

NAMES
English: *Spider - different names for different species or families;*
             Baboon spider, Daddy Longlegs, Tarantula, etc.
Afrikaans: *Spinnekop.*
African: *ulwembu (Z), segoku (N-S)*

DISTRIBUTION: Worldwide except for the Polar deserts.

DIET: All spiders are carnivorous. Most eat insects while some have specialised diets such as ants, or fish and tadpoles. Most spiders are cannibalistic.

FEATURES AND HABITS: There are some 4 ,000 species of spiders in the world, belonging to roughly 30 different families. They have become marvellously adapted to the different environments which they exploit. A great variety of shapes, sizes, colours and camouflaging is found. Like other *Arachnida,* spiders have four pairs of legs. Some spiders are blind but most have some form of eye. A unique feature is the possession of abdominal spinnerets which spin silk, used in nest building, fashioning cocoons and webs, and binding prey. The variety and ingenuity in webs is endless; enormous wheel-shaped webs with radiating spokes between trees, horizontal webs over streams, silk-lined underground tubes with trap-doors, etc. Not all spiders spin webs; wolf-spiders or *Lycosidae* hunt on the ground and jump on their prey like carnivores. All except four kinds are solitary and extremely unsociable in their habits. Almost all spiders have poison-glands but very few have a bite dangerous to man - the only exception in South Africa is the 'button-spider'. Another dangerous species is the tropical Black Widow. After mating the male dies or is devoured by the female. How and where the eggs are laid and hatched depends on the species. Egg cocoons are common and these are often carried around, or guarded by the mother. Spiders eat millions of insects annually and play an important role in preserving the balance of nature.

SPIDER

No spider struggles to create
The beautiful. His tensile arc
Knows mathematics in the dark;
A Michael Angelo of air
Who weaves a theory that states
Ultimatums on a hair.

Born to the purple of his need
He has no unsolved problems. He
Suffers no dichotomy,

214

But wakes to work and works to kill;
Beauty empiric in his greed,
Perfection in a villain's skill.

Ragblown summit of the ooze
Of soft warm mud that split and stirred —
I hold within my skull the work
Sealed and socketed; yet my hands
Fashion with artifice and ruse
Not wily web, but witless strands.

But when the poor cold corpse of words
Is laid upon its candled bier,
I, vindicate, will shed the tear
That falls like wax, and creep unheard
To weave in silence, grave and bowed,
The pure necessity — a shroud.

Ruth Miller

TARANTULA

Such is your fate tarantula
for emerging red-claw raised between my pillows
so early in the morning to ambush my nerves
I lost my decision awhile as the space
I knew so well diminished in the search
for weapons - books, combs, and chairs.

Your hands and legs - pedipalps - bend to your face
with the pain of the spray-bursts held so long
like a fire extinguisher. How are you dead
when my ankles and my hind-arm
still echo my fears with aching burning?

Such repose, Arachnida, your unsuspecting fate
for tenderly - stealthily - endlessly searching
for prey and resting nooks in human surroundings.

Your long, hairy legs interlock -
finally, stiff.

Masaemura Bonas Zimunya

215

JUMPING SPIDER

With swift, spry, delicate or bunched--alertings
He moves, a feather on the bench, reconnoitring
His eye, almost hairy, swivels pore-sensitive
While a rut in the wood spurs him, sleight of hand
Three-four inches forward
Where he waits, the poison of his truth, probing.

To be so constantly aware and nervous-vigilant
Betokens, I have found, a sizzling respect
For all life's identities set disparately in motion
And a cognizance that some will way-lay you.
So much is different, so much fraught and able
(He seems to say), to be solid or deaf is the true unreality.

His black and patient irregularity is like a grip
Geigering the book of leaves, the spread of atoms
Whirling in sun-slim air; though a shilling can cover him
His passionate sanity would carry a mint away
Were rewards given to those nearest the cunning thread of life,
The web we so briefly penetrate before we die.

What priest ever crosses himself at Holy Mass
As he sideways, bisects the hope of a previous track?
What scientist, scrupulous with hypothesis
Accepts such quick and irretrievable points of rest?
He scrambles the compass to spin the radius of each second:
It stops, and he clomps, applauding with a mandible jaw.

Perseus Adams

The spider sucks poison from the same flower that a bee sucks honey.
Evil natures find food in the same places as good. There's nothing
good or bad but thinking makes it so!

S

SPRINGBOK *Antidorcas marsupialis*

NAMES
English: *Springbok*
Afrikaans: *Springbok*
African: *insephe (Z), tshepe (N-S)*

DISTRIBUTION: Today only on fenced off farms in parts of South Africa, but still abundant in parts of Botswana, the Kalahari, Namibia and southern Angola. They were once extremely common in the grasslands and semi-arid regions of South Africa.

DIET: They are both browsers and grazers and particularly fond of young grass and shoots. They will dig out roots and bulbs when food is scarce and can survive indefinitely without water.

FEATURES AND HABITS: The best-known antelope of southern Africa and the national emblem of South African sport. The most usual colour is a reddish-fawn with white markings on the face, inside legs, underbody and tail. Some chocolate brown and even albino specimens occur. When frightened or in high spirits they start 'pronking'. With the head bent down and the back arched they leap 2 to 3 metres into the air in stiff-legged jumps. At the same time the long white hair of the dorsal area is raised in a conspicuous crest. Springbok herds vary in size depending on the season and availability of food. In the past, when springbok were still abundant and the farms not fenced in, mass migrations by herds of thousands took place in response to environmental conditions. Springbok are preyed upon by all the carnivores and the young are also caught by large eagles. Territories are maintained by dominant males during the mating season. Although fighting does occur, injury or death is rare. One lamb per ewe is born during the rainy season and synchronisation of births in a herd takes place so that predators cannot cope with the glut of vulnerable lambs.

SPRINGBOKS

In the dawn-light blue they scatter the dew
From their flanks as they gambol on the grey Karoo.

They feed and stray; take fright — flash away —
And the pack that follows is a dun dust-spray:

Half-buck, half-bird! — the veld is stirred
With the flashing ripple of that racing herd!

As dolphins play, hooping irised spray,
These curved, leaping racers loop air with clay:

218

Footballers, they shun their shadows and run
Heading-and-heeling-at the red, round sun:

Brown breakers, they curl and their white manes hurl
At a beach — none may reach — the horizon's pearl.

F.C. Slater

'These beautiful and peaceful little antelopes once drifted across the
uplands of Africa in countless millions ... Because of excessive increase
... armies of them, pressed shoulder to shoulder, would take days to
pass a given point ... In one case they even pressed on into the sea,
so that a long stretch of the coast in Namibia was piled with their
bodies.' (Ivan T. Sanderson, *Living Mammals of the World*, p263)

The totem animal of white South Africans, worshipped with religious
fervour by young and old. Also a species of rugby footballers, by no
means as beautiful or swift as the small antelope, at present frustrated
in their ambition to win the world title by a universal conspiracy of
envious spoilsports. In recent matches they have displayed vicious
Yahoo tendencies.

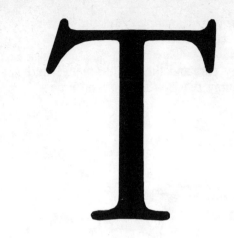

TORTOISE Class *Reptilia* Order *Chelonia*

NAMES
English: *Tortoise and turtle respectively for terrestial and aquatic species. They are closely related.*
Afrikaans:*Skilpad and Waterskilpad*
African: *ufudu (Z), ufudu lwaso-lwandle(Z).*
Scientific: Family *Testudinidae - land species*
Family *Pelomedusidae - water species*

220

DISTRIBUTION: Temperate zones of the world. Throughout Africa.

DIET: Land tortoises are herbivorous but do sometimes eat the dung of carnivores and bones, presumably for the mineral contents. Water tortoises (turtles) are carnivorous, eating fish, insects, frogs, small mammals as well as carrion.

FEATURES AND HABITS: The soft body parts of all tortoises are enclosed in a hard, protective case of horn-covered bone. The head and legs can be withdrawn for protection and the jaws are toothless but covered with a horny sheath which provides a sharp cutting edge. The shells of tortoises are marked with geometrically arranged, radiating patterns usually in muted browns, blacks, yellowish-whites and olives. Patterns, colours and the actual shape of the shell vary between species. Tortoises and turtles vary from a few grams in weight to as much as 500 kg in some of the giants such as the Galapagos and leatherback species. They have many enemies: man, who collects them illegally as pets or finds the eggs as well as the animal (roasted in its own shell) a rare gastronomic treat; birds, who break the shell by hammering holes through it or dropping the tortoise from a height in order to get to the soft body parts; carnivores, birds and rodents who dig out the eggs. Being reptiles, and therefore 'cold-blooded', tortoises cannot tolerate extremes of temperatures - in winter they hibernate and in the heat of summer they take refuge in the shade. They are the longest living vertebrates - ages of 125 years having been verified. Adult males become aggressive during the mating season and rival suitors are butted and pushed in an attempt to overturn and so incapacitate the adversary. All land, as well as water tortoises, lay their eggs in holes dug in the ground by the female and then left to incubate without further care. Depending on weather conditions this can take from a few months to two years. When the young hatch they are extremely vulnerable and easily preyed upon. Comparatively few reach maturity.

MOUNTAIN TORTOISE

The years contract in his eye:
to withered neck, sciatic limp
reduced, and yet enlarged above
the boundary of mortality.
Generations (like a summer's day)
flash past: Egypt, Babylon

rise from the dust again:
Rameses to battle goes –
but the war-helm lies in the ash
of a dusty, of a grey
primordial Karoo.

Ernst van Heerden
Trans. Richard Harvey

THE TORTOISE

He sought longevity; vegetarian
He cut pale leaves of clover with bony gums
On the hill-side. Having mastered this art,
Found he could feed on invisible influences
In the atmosphere, scent-essences and ghosts.
His membrained nose sucked in the pure ice,
Greyish-blue tinted, aetherized, of mountain air.
Like a fish winter-bound
Hibernated, bloodless.

Next turned to imitate the life of stones.
Brilliant impurities in his clay
Rose streaking to the surface and were combed
To consistent sheens. On the sea's bed
Became inured to pressure, that laid rings
On him, flake pressed down upon flake.
Or in temporary release, uplifted,
Things outside this world, the seven stars,
Aurora borealis, imprinted
Blue flickering strands on his charmed loins,
Learnt to be composite, humped with embedded stones,
Petrified wood, animal skeleton, sand.

Was rock. Only, always,
At the base of his throat,
Like a bubble in purple lava
Rolling, horrible,
Without escape, his pulse.

Peter Strauss

THE TORTOISE AND THE HARE

This our land,
They the tortoise,
We, the hare
Dark and white
The races
Life
The race

We are educated
We qualify
Jobs await us
We employ
Superior facilities
We enjoy

Riots
We suppress
The media
We direct
Our interests
We protect

We build great buildings
We teach
We write our feelings
We preach
But all the while
We sleep

How can
The tortoise
Possibly
Win?

Berin N. Gilfillan

Charova sei chando chakwidza hamba mumuti.

How severe the frost must have been that made the tortoise climb a tree.

i.e. People do impossible things in an emergency.

Shona

Khudu-tlou e robetse bo lobeto ba ipha naga.
The giant-tortoise is asleep and the little ones graze where they like.
When the cat's away, the mice will play.

Khudu ea mariga e itsioe ke mmei.
The winter lair of the tortoise is known only to the keeper.
He that hides can find.

Sechuana

U

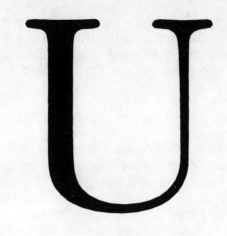

UNICORN Genera *Monocerotibus* - two species, according to Pliny the Elder (23 - 79 A.D.); *timidum* and *beluarum periculosissimum*. First described by Ctesias (400 B.C.).

NAMES
English: *Unicorn*
Afrikaans:*Eenhoring*

DISTRIBUTION: Extinct or mythical? The persistent occurrence of this creature in folklore traditions all over the world, places it in the realm of fringe biology - on the borderline between a real and a phenomenal existence, together with others such as the Loch Ness Monster, the Yeti and the Tokoloshe.

DIET: Nothing is known about its diet, but see poem 'Grass for the Unicorn'.

FEATURES AND HABITS: Varies greatly depending on species. Pliny, in his *Inventorum Natura,* described the species *timidum* as timid and fleet of foot, resembling a goat or antelope but with a single sharp horn projecting from its forehead. This could be a description of a ewe of the Duiker family. (See also entry under Duiker). The species *beluarum periculosissimum* was extremely dangerous and impossible to capture alive. It has an armoured hide and one very long horn. Kings and nobles paid high prices for the horn from which goblets were carved which neutralised poisons. The powdered horn was also a cure for all ailments. The similarities between this description of a unicorn and a rhinoceros are too obvious to ignore. Please see entry under rhinoceros. The amazing tooth of the unicorn whale (narwhal) is also legend provoking. It forms a spiral tusk, up to 2.7 metre long and probably led many an old time mariner in the Arctic to believe that he had found a unicorn horn. By the Middle Ages the unicorn had variously become a symbol of virginity and Christianity. It is said that if a young virgin was placed in his haunt the animal lay down with his head in her lap and so became easy prey to hunters. Mediaeval writers described the unicorn as having the legs of a buck, the tail of a lion, the head and body of a horse and, of course, a single horn in the middle of its forehead. It can only be hoped that like the supposedly long extinct Coelacanth, the real unicorn (whatever it is) will make a spontaneous reappearance soon. Until then we will have to be satisfied to see the unicorn only as a heraldic beast, decorating the arms of countries such as Great Britain and families such as Smith, Stewart, Burgers and Bergh.

THE UNICORN

There are unicorns.
I haven't seen them myself
but others have, reliable men
who write in books, in newspapers.
Once, travellers told

of blue-eyed unicorns with barber's pole horns
that raced in deserts, visited virgins in dreams.
There's even talk of a unicorn
that walked down Adderley Street,
through a department store,
and speaking a mixture of English and Greek,
ordered nectar at the milk bar.
Someone asked for its autograph:
a father, eyeing that horn,
hauled his daughter away;
an elderley woman, beneath a black hat,
wanted to call Someone:
'It looks like a foreign idea'.
(The unicorn sniffed its coke).
Then the men from the Natural History Museum came.

Robert Greig

THE UNICORN

The Unicorn
is full of resurrections
prancing supreme
over all our myths.
He prongs death
into the ditch
of its own lie
rising again
with triumphant horn.
Over the rooftops
of our sheltered lives
he dances glibly
out of reach
while we strive to catch
his posture
for an emblem.
Over the bomb shelters
of our fears
he trots
rampant
against a field azure

while the lion
lies down
with a ruffled mane
in a tired heraldic pose.

Bruce Hewett

THE SAILING OF THE ARK

The sky was low, the sounding rain was falling dense and dark,
And Noah's sons were standing at the window of the Ark.

The beasts were in, but Japhet said, 'I see one creature more
Belated and unmated there comes knocking at the door.'

'Well, let him knock, or let him drown' said Ham, 'or learn to swim;
We're overcrowded as it is. We've got no room for him.'

'And yet it knocks. How terribly it knocks,' said Shem. 'Its feet
Are hard as horns. And O, the air from it is sweet.'

'Now hush!' said Ham, 'You'll waken Dad, and once he comes to see
What's at the door, it's sure to mean more work for you and me.'

Noah's voice came roaring from the darkness down below:
'Some animal is knocking. Let it in before we go.'

Ham shouted back (and savagely he nudged the other two)
'That's only Japhet knocking down a bradnail in his shoe.'

Said Noah, 'Boys, I hear a noise that's like a horse's hoof.'
Said Ham, 'Why, that's the dreadful rain that drums upon the roof.'

Noah tumbled up on deck, and out he puts his head.
His face grew white, his knees were loosed, he tore his beard and said,

'Look, look! It would not wait. It turns away. It takes its flight.
Fine work you've made of it, my sons, between you all to-night.

O noble and unmated beast, my sons were all unkind.
In such a night, what stable and what manger will you find?

228

O golden hoofs, O cataracts of mane, O nostrils wide
With high disdain, and O the neck wave-arched, the lovely pride!

O long shall be the furrows ploughed upon the hearts of men
Before it comes to stable and to manger once again.

And dark and crooked all the roads in which our race will walk,
And shrivelled all their manhood like a flower on broken stalk.

Now all the world, O Ham, may curse the hour that you were born -
Because of you, the Ark must sail without the Unicorn.'

C.S. Lewis

GRASS FOR THE UNICORN

Sheep may safely graze, earth bound cows
                do likewise.
Shaking in my boots, I pass them
                  by, I am drawn
to a riskier animal, a fabled beast
                   who has outgrown

utility-unless the pang he brings,
                    the pointed summary
the cloudy mesmeric journeying
                    unwinding
the fields of tenderness, the landscape of care
be looked on in that way.

He rests at the foot of a gaunt, much-
                    eroded stone,
so lean with neglect, you'd think he
                    grew right out
of it, if it wasn't for the towering
                    horn, the dark
sheen of his kindling eyes ... the way
                    he's so
steeped in light as to appear
                    porous.
In a pasture of sparse, numinous
words, he outlandishly blinks, he
quietly lords it, shrugs off your worldly
                    rank, the herds
who sleep snugly in rooms or kraals
                    complaisant
to their yoke. Our glances lock.
                    I enter
the realm of singing fact, the place
                    where insight
comes in a flash. He lifts a
                    moss-encrusted
hoof, many insects tune the taut
harps of his flanks, the white shade

of his high superfluousness. I feed him a head-line
                    and he sniffs.
I offer him a rose from my boxed emotions
and the great horn dips slightly, the tail
                    flicks.
Finally, holding back nothing, I
                    reach in
and give him an image chopped
                    from my bones.

230

This time he chews, his pleasure
a fire that adorns the cold hillside.

I want to give him a poem that will
                          make him
                          run like
                                the wind

Perseus Adams

'A fabulous beast born of man's imagination, the unicorn plays a
leading role in some of his most ancient myths and legends. It's form
and function are as variable as the minds and religions of men; but
whatever its shape … a one-horned beast was always a symbol of
supreme power, connected with gods and kings. It concentrates into a
single horn the vigour and virility associated with the two horns of real
animals! *(Man, Myth and Magic,* London: Marshall Cavendish, 1970)

In the Middle Ages it came to represent Christ. It was believed to be
alive in Southern Africa during the early nineteenth century. Governors
offered a reward for positive proof of its existence.

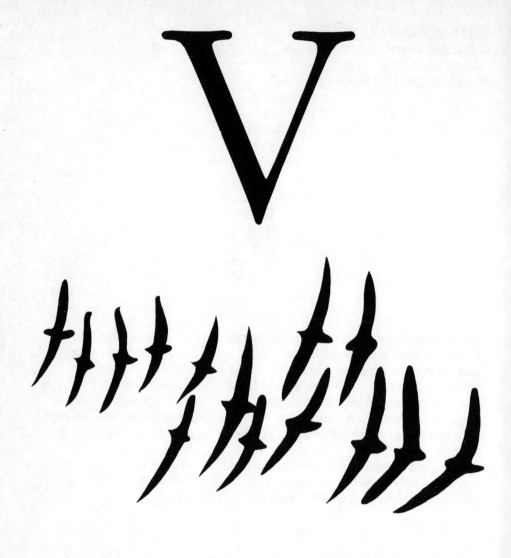

VULTURE Family *Aegypiidae* - Six or seven species found in Africa.

NAMES
English: *Vulture, and depending on characteristics of species referred to; Cape -, White-backed -, Lapped-face -, Egyptian - etc.*
Afrikaans: *Aasvoel; Krans -, Witrug- , Swart- , Egipties -, etc.*
African: *inqe (Z), le-Aka (S), Isilwangangubo (X), Inkqo (X).*

DISTRIBUTION: Except for the Cape Vulture which is found in most of southern Africa (absent from the Kalahari) the other species are to day rarely found south of the Orange River but spread out across Africa, some as far as southern Europe.

DIET: They are scavengers and eat mostly carrion. Some also eat offal, insects, small reptiles and fish. The Palm-nut vulture eats the husks of oil and raffia palms but there is continued argument whether this species is in fact a true vulture and not an eagle.

FEATURES AND HABITS: Except for the Palm-nut vulture all vultures have heads at least partially bare of feathers. Some, especially young birds, may have a down covering on the head. They are exceptionally strong fliers and have wonderful eyesight. They soar to great heights in search of carrion and it is accepted that they watch each other carefully so that if one spots a dead animal all the others will see him start the descent. This explains why hundreds of birds, of different species, will congregate near a carcass in the shortest possible time. Eating sessions like this takes place amid much fighting and noise. Hooded- and Egyptian vultures also haunt villages, slaughter yards and refuse dumps for food. Vultures have relatively weak claws, not adapted to hold prey, but a powerful beak suited to tear skin and flesh from the toughest carcass. Cape vultures are known to attack sheep and others such as the white headed species have also been observed killing fair-sized prey of their own. Some species are today in danger of becoming extinct - they are destroyed by farmers in retaliation for killing sheep and sometimes accidently poisoned. They build big nests of sticks in trees or lay their eggs on ledges of inaccessible precipices, usually on the bare rock. Larger vultures normally lay one egg and smaller ones two.

THE WOMAN WHO WAS A SISTER TO VULTURES

A woman of the early race
took vultures for her sisters.
They lived with her and ate with her,
they did not eat a little.

The woman's husband brought a gnu
which he had killed while hunting.
The vultures, flapping, swallowed it;
they ate up all the gnu's flesh.

The woman took the skin for food.
She singed it and she boiled it.
When it was soft, she went to call
her man to eat the gnu's skin.

While she was gone the vultures took
hold of the skin, they pulled it.
They tore it and they swallowed it,
though they had eaten gnu's flesh.

The woman and her man came back.
He was the hungry husband.
He cursed the birds, he threatened them,
for he was very angry.

The vultures were afraid of him.
They fled in all directions.
They flew to sit on trees and stones
And watched their sister's husband.

The husband went to hunt again.
He pierced a gnu, he tracked it.
When it was dead, he brought it home.
The man was tired, he rested.

The day was hot, he fell asleep.
The vultures saw him sleeping.
They did not fear his wife who was
a woman and their sister.

Therefore they rose, they flew, they came,
they swallowed up the gnu's flesh.
They ate in haste, they went to sit
beyond the flight of arrows.

For they knew well, when he woke up,
the man would wish to pierce them.
The man, awaking, saw afar
the vultures and he cursed them.

"Ye who are sisters of my wife,
I can no more endure ye.
Ye are the ones that make us starve,
destruction be upon ye."

The woman also spoke to them:
"Ye take our food - chabbabbu!
Ye are no longer sisters who
may come to fill their bellies."

Therefore we do not take again
she-vultures for our sisters.
Indeed, we kill them while we wish
that we might not go hungry.

Bushman, as told by Arthur Markowitz

VULTURE

On ragged black sails
he soars hovering over
everything and death;
a blight in the eye
of the stunning sun.

An acquisitive droop
of beak, head and neck
dangles, dully angling,
a sentient pendulum
next to his keeled chest.

His eyes peer, piously
bloodless and hooded,
far-sighted, blighting
grasses, trees, hill-passes,
stones, streams, bones, bleached bones

with the tacky rags
of flesh adherent.
A slow ritual fold
of candid devil's palms
in blasphemous prayer —

235

the still wings sweep closed –
the hyena of skies
plummets from the pulpit
of a tall boredom,
swallowing as he falls.

He brakes lazily
before his back breaks
to settle on two
creaky final wing-beats
flinging twin dust-winds.

He squats once fearfully.
Flushed with unhealthy plush
and pregustatory
satisfaction, head back,
he jumps lumpishly up.

Slack neck with the pecked
skin thinly shaking, he
sidles aside, then stumps
his deliberate banker's
gait to the stinking meal.

Douglas Livingstone

VULTURES

Below the krantz the heat stops
And in the shadow
Cracked bones and feathers pile.
Cold water oozes from the rock.

Dropped from its nest
A hundred feet above
A young bird hangs
Suspended from a bush.

Carrion already, the breast
Trembles under flies;
The beak gapes
In rictus.

236

It is as though
Some horror
Of your own, had falling,
Snapped its ugly neck.

Look close. Then go.
Walk into the heat,
Look into the light as though
All light had just begun.

Against blue air
The vultures circle,
Turning like flies
Across the sun.

Patrick Cullinan

BUSHVELD BALLET

Obliquely ribs an old and molten sun
The jungle decor of the Bush, where dies
The kudu bull, compassion's leaden prize.
Aloof, the jackals lick their thoughts, for none
Would eat before the lion had begun.
Black-ruffled ballerinas from the skies —
To drain the sockets of his empty eyes —
Effect a leggy landing, one by one.

Now lives the bushveld's dire choreography
In arabesque and attitude, sequence
Of dripping entrails whose festooning lilt
Betrays the bleeding core of gallantry.
Appalled by this rank masque of innocence
I long to love my sane, deliberate guilt.

Cythna Letty

Lapho kukhon' isidumbu, yilapho kukhon' amanqe.
Where the carcass is, there the vultures will be.

Vultures are known to be scavengers. When an animal dies in the veld, they quickly spot it and consume the dead body.

There are many people who behave like vultures. They always watch for the downfall of others, in the hope of getting some pickings. It is like the relatives of a deceased person, who suddenly emerge from nowhere in the hope of benefitting by the death of their dead relation.

Zulu

WILDCAT *Felis lybica*

NAMES
English: *African Wild Cat*
Afrikaans: *Vaalboskat*
African: *imbodla, impaka (Z)*

DISTRIBUTION: Throughout Africa but absent from tropical forests and deserts. It prefers slightly wooded surroundings and where this is not available, long grass.

DIET: Adaptable and therefore able to survive in many different surroundings. Primarily rodents but will also eat birds, reptiles, insects and fruit. In settled areas it preys on poultry and even lambs.

FEATURES AND HABITS: The African wildcat probably belongs to the same species which was domesticated by the Egyptians some 3,500 years ago. It looks a lot like an ordinary domestic tabby cat but is bigger. The most important differences are its longer legs which give it a distinctive gait, a shorter tail and the rufous colour behind its ears. The fur is grey to yellowish grey. Its body is indistinctly marked with wavy, vertical stripes while the foreparts of the chest and underbody are of a paler colour and spotted. It is a solitary, shy, nocturnal animal and seldom seen by day. It hunts singly, in pairs and sometimes in small family groups. Like all true cats it stalks or ambushes its prey and then jumps on it for the kill. It does interbreed with domestic cats and is in danger of becoming hybridised in some areas. Crossbred kittens remain fierce and untrustworthy but can become more domesticated than some of the other 'wild cat' breeds such as the Small Spotted Cat or the Caracal. Mating is accompanied by the same screeching and caterwauling as in domestic cats. An average of three kittens is born during summer.

GENTLING A WILDCAT

Not much wild life, roared Mine leonine Host
from the fringe of a forest of crackles
round an old dome-headed steam radio,
between hotel and river — a mile of bush —
except for the wildcats and jackals.

And he, of these parts for years, was right.
That evening I ventured with no trepidations
and a torch, towed by the faculty
I cannot understand, that has got me
into too many situations.

Under a tree, in filtered moonlight,
a ragged heap of dusty leaves stopped moving.
A cat lay there, open from chin to loins;
lower viscera missing; truncated tubes
and bitten-off things protruding.

Little blood there was, but a mess of
damaged lungs; straining to hold its breath
for quiet; claws fixed curved and jutting,
jammed open in a stench of jackal meat;
it tried to raise its head hating the mystery, death.

The big spade-skull with its lynx-fat cheeks
aggressive still, raging eyes hooked in me, game;
nostrils pulling at a tight mask of anger
and fear; then I remembered hearing
they are quite impossible to tame.

Closely, in a bowl of unmoving roots,
an untouched carcass, unlicked, swaddled and wrapped
in trappings of birth, the first of a litter stretched.
Rooted out in midconfinement: a time
when jackals have courage enough for a wildcat.

In some things too, I am a coward,
and could not here punch down with braced thumb,
lift the nullifying stone or stiff-edged hand
to axe with mercy the nape of her spine.
Besides, I convinced myself, she was numb.

And oppressively, something felt wrong:
not her approaching melting with earth,
but in lifetimes of claws, kaleidoscopes:
moon-claws, sun-claws, teeth after death,
certainly both at mating and birth.

So I sat and gentled her with my hand,
not moving much but saying things, using my voice;
and she became gentle, affording herself
the influent luxury of breathing —
untrammelled, bubbly, safe in its noise.

Later, calmed, despite her tides of pain,
she let me ease her claws, the ends of the battle,
pulling off the trapped and rancid flesh.
Her miniature limbs of iron relaxed.
She died with hardly a rattle.

I placed her peaceful ungrinning corpse
and that of her firstborn in the topgallants
of a young tree, out of ground reach, to grow: restart
a cycle of maybe something more pastoral,
commencing with beetles, then maggots, then ants.

Douglas Livingstone

WHAT'S LEFT OF A WILDCAT?

Wildcat caught
in the spotlight
of my poem,
eyes staring anger
at me blind
behind the light.

Now on his face a grin
(of pain?)
as under the aim
of my intent
his body's ripped
to syllables.

Is the head
(rigid, life-
less, still
grinning)
worth mounting on paper
walls of my world?

Charl J.F. Cilliers

Udlel' emkhombeni wempaka.
He eats out of the wild cat's dish.

The impaka was always associated with witchcraft. It was regarded,
and still is regarded, as the medium of the wizards. People have their
utensils for eating, and the dish of a witch's cat is certainly not a dish
to eat out of.

This saying is used of a person who is impolite in speech and actions.

Zulu

243

WILDEBEEST *Connochaetes taurinus*

NAMES
English: *Blue Wildebeest, Wildebeest, brindled gnu*
Afrikaans: *Blouwildebees(t)*
African: *inkonkoni (Z)*

DISTRIBUTION: Much wider distribution than the gnu (black wildebeest) - northern parts of southern Africa such as the Transvaal Lowveld and the Kalahari and north through East Africa to the Equator.

DIET: They are exclusively grazers and eat only short grass.

FEATURES AND HABITS: Larger than the gnu but with the same ungainly, ill-proportioned look about it - a massive head, sloping back and comparatively thin legs. In spite of this the wildebeest is surprisingly fleet-footed. It has dark greyish-brown hair with indistinct vertical stripes which in some light conditions does have a bluish-grey sheen. The black beard-like tuft below its chin, bunches of hair on the face and its wild-looking eyes give the wildebeest a deranged expression. They are gregarious animals and sometimes form herds of several hundreds but normally up to twenty or thirty. On cool days they remain active but when it is hot they crowd together in the shade of trees. They are often seen with other animals such as zebra or impala. Larger, mixed herds have a better chance of spotting danger. The zebras eat the longer grass and leave the shorter grass to the wildebeest. In turn the zebras benefit because predators prefer to catch wildebeest. When alarmed the wildebeest gives vent to much snorting, races off only to stop suddenly and turn to face the intruder. They are tenacious and tough and will put up quite a fight when wounded. Wildebeest are often seen disporting themselves in a thoroughly mad way leaping, prancing and kicking their heels up in the air. During the rut one to three bulls establish a territory and to keep the cows within its boundaries. Calves are born around mid-summer and are subject to heavy predation.

ROCK ART

Blue wildebeest look cross.
They hump a bag of rocks
within their thick shoulders.
They shake uncombed fringes.

But they have a weakness,
it seems, in the forelegs.
They run, bob, stumble, as
if on knees and knuckles.

Eight centuries ago
a little Bushman boy
and strange, became friends with
a small wildebeest calf.

Each having offended
his tribe by the friendship,
they were both driven forth.
The very ground was torn.

A certain rock painting
shows the boy as anti-
social. The criminal
was chased and stoned when seen.

Long-buttocked hunters one
day cornered him and then
killed him in the prescribed
manner. The calf escaped.

The calf, one observes next,
grew older, fought bulls, raped
the strayed cows at the edge
of his ancestral herd.

As his stature increased
his outlaw's existence
grew a choked volcano
on now-cubist shoulders.

From here and there he glared
redly through the forest
of his mane, while standing
snorting tall black thunders.

Perhaps his rage really
eclipsed the sun's fury.
It is almost certain
the weak forelegs remained.

The boy's spirit became
a shadow on the moon.
Times were pitiless, rough,
The code has not changed much.

The series ends with the
beast trampling with its knees
tribesmen in the throes of
worshipping this new god.

Douglas Livingstone

The scarcity of representation of the wildebeest in the Drakensberg has been remarked on by one or two observers but particularly by Vinnicombe who has suggested that it is deliberate avoidance, paralleling the Bushman custom of avoidance of in-laws - a custom which reduced friction in daily living (Vinnicombe, 1976, p.209).

This suggestion is supported by the story of why the black wildebeest has a light tail. The story describes how people known as the longnosed mice tried to hunt quagga by the traditional method of planting ostrich feather wands and lying in wait behind a screen of bushes. They were thwarted by the intervention of a wildebeest which blunted their arrows, made their bowstrings slack and trampled one of them to death. It did this by disguising itself with a tail of grass which resembled the tails of the quaggas.

It was Kaggen who realised what was happening and persuaded cleverer people - the striped-mice - to take the place of the long-nosed mice. The striped-mice people substituted new arrowheads for those that had been blunted, tightened the bowstings and built separate little screens of bushes behind which they hid, away from the obvious hiding places. By this means they were able to kill many quagga and also to kill the wildebeest by shooting him through the armpits - a place which would destroy his magic powers. At that the wildebeest snatched out the grass tail, hurled it away and lay down to die (Bleek, 1932, p.58).

So the wildebeest was hostile to man, it herded with zebra or quagga and ostrich and confused hunting procedures. It was an animal to be avoided - and so it was rarely painted. Its light tail did, however, provide hairs for paint brushes. (Ellenberger, 1953, p.87)

Woodhouse

X

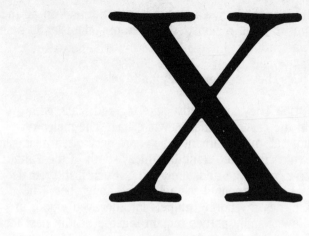

XYLOCOPA *Order Hymenoptera, Super-family Apoidea. Some 10,000 species of bees are known in the world.*

NAMES
English: *carpenter bee*
Afrikaans: *hout(kapper)by*
African: *zingizi Shona*
Scientific: Family *Xylocopidae*

DISTRIBUTION: Fairly cosmopolitan. Carpenter bees are found on all the continents - though not in polar regions. Absent from some islands such as Great Britain.

DIET: Like all other bees they feed on honey and pollen.

FEATURES AND HABITS: They are mostly quite big and black with bands of yellow or, in the case of females, white hair. The males of some species are yellow all over. Carpenter bees are very often mistaken for bumble bees, of which there are none in Africa, south of the Sahara. They are not aggressive by nature and rarely sting. Even if the female does sting the pain is slight compared to that of the honey bee. The carpenter bee makes its nest by boring tunnels into decayed wood, or tree-stumps, with its jaw. Family parties remain together in the nest for most of the year. When the breeding season arrives, the females drive the males out. After mating the male dies.

XYLOCOPA - CARPENTER BEE - ZINGIZI

Pimbirimano was afraid of Hyena
So he blew his fear into his flute.
'Flute, is it safe to pick tomatoes
Down by the edge of the stream?'

'Pimbirimano', buzzed the flute
Softly on its lowest note,
'You are right to be uncertain.
I'll call Zingizi the carpenter bee
To inspect the tomatoes down by the stream.'

'I'm Zingizi
The Carpenter Bee,
A bee
But a bee with a difference?
That's me!
Other bees only appear when
There's stinging on the agenda.
But I, Zingizi,
Can boast of more than a sting.'

250

Black and gold in his first team rugby jersey
Zingizi zoomed over the patch of green.
Among the red of the glossy tomatoes
He spied the spotty hyena's head.
'I see you, you smelly son of a witch.
Get going, or I'll sting you where it's very sore.'
'Sting as you wish', laughed the hairy hyena.

Zingizi circled
      Round and down,
'I'm going to sting you in the nape of your neck!'
'Sting as you wish, my fur is thick,'
           laughed that spotty hyena.

Zingizi circled
      Round and down,
      Down and round.
'I'm going to sting you in the small of your back!'
'Sting as you wish, my skin is thick,'
           laughed that spotty hyena.

Zingizi circled
      Round and down,
      Down and round.
      Round and down,
Making that spotted hyena giddy.
'I'm going to sting you, now, where it hurts most.'
'Sting as you wish, I'm sitting down!'
           but before he could laugh this time
Zingizi stung him, deep, on the tip of his nasty nose.

When Pimbirimano saw Hyena
Running in circles fast as he could
For the horrible wastes of the Kalahari
He played on his flute which sang
'With my flute
And my friend Zingizi
Picking tomatoes is easy.'

Guy Butler

The Carpenter Bee - Zingizi.

Of all insects, this is most often found in stories - it has some
personality of its own. When bees are found they are there because
stinging is on the agenda. The zingizi has other talents beside stinging.

Shona

Y

A SCHOLARLY NOTE

The Yahoo was first made known to science by Dr Lemuel Gulliver, M.B.Ch.B.(Cantab. and Leiden). The Fourth Book of *Gulliver's Travels* (London, 1726) remains the starting point for all students of the species, and it is a matter of concern to serious primatologists that Leaky, Broome and Tobias have chosen to ignore his work.

Victim of a mutiny in May 1611, Gulliver was set ashore on an unknown island in the Indian Ocean, where, due to the operations of natural selection, a species of horse, known as Houyhnhms (*Equus Rationalis*)had gained an ascendency over all other creatures, including the Yahoos, large primates who lived a subservient and graceless life beneath them.

> 'Their Head and Breasts were covered with thick Hair, some frizzled and others lank; they had beards like Goats, and a long Ridge of hair down their Backs, and the fore parts of Legs and Feet; but the rest of their bodies were bare, so that I might see their skins which were of a Buff Colour. They had no Tails, nor any Hair at all on their Buttocks, except about the *Anus;* which I presume Nature had placed there to defend them as they sat on the Ground; for this Posture they used, as well as by lying down, and often stood on their hind feet. They climbed high trees, as nimbly as a squirrel, for they had strong extended Claws before and behind terminating in sharp points, hooked. They would often spring, and bound, and leap, with the greatest agility.'

They were omnivorous. 'I saw three of those detestable creatures ... feeding upon Roots and the Flesh of some Animals.' They were dirty, ugly, vicious, lecherous, greedy and unteachable, and without allies or friends in nature. 'He observed every Animal in the Country naturally to abhor the Yahoos, whom the Weaker avoided, and the Stronger drove from them'. Living before Darwin, Dr Gulliver may have over-reacted when forced to acknowledge that these creatures were higher primates, and very like himself.

> 'My Horror and Astonishment are not to be described, when I observed in this abominable Animal a perfect human Figure;... The Fore-feet of the Yahoo differed from my hands in nothing else but the length of the

Nails, the Coarseness and Brownness of the Palms, and the Hairiness on the Backs. There was the same resemblance between our feet...'

He sought reassurance in the fact that these creatures lacked higher technology, such as fire and explosives, language and law, and above all, the faculty of reason. The sub-species, *Homo sapiens Anglicanus,* of which he was proud to be a member, possessed all these amply. He was, after all, living in the Age of Reason. But, having explained to his equine master the murderous uses to which the higher primates of Europe were putting their technology, and their endemic misuse of language for deceit, he was told that it was ludicrous for a creature who so abused nature's every gift and faculty to lay claim to reason. Indeed, it seems that the Doctor's eloquent defence of European Civilisation was the last straw for the rational horses, who politely arranged for his reluctant departure from their country, after a sojourn of three years. The Doctor's experiences on returning to England did nothing to negate his horror at the traces of Yahoo behaviour he discovered in himself, in his family, and in the civilised world.

Sceptics may ask 'Where is the Island?' It has disappeared, (as islands sometimes do; witness Krakatoa, in a violent volcanic explosion in 1870), but not before Yahoos had gained a firm foothold on the mainland, where, unrestrained by *Equus Rationalis,* they have rapidly increased to the deepening despair of ecologists. Cunning as always, they soon learnt to wear clothes and to shave, and so became undistinguishable, except to the discriminating, in a crowd. They proved quite as vicious and greedy as *Homo Sapiens,* with the same compulsion to exterminate other species. (See *Quagga*). A rare creature in the eighteenth century, the Yahoo is now as common as dirt, incapable of controlling his lusts and hatreds, polluting the habitat, a threat and a danger to all other forms of life. Some argue that he has gained the whip hand of *Homo Sapiens* by rising to his level; others argue that Man has sunk into Yahoodom. It matters little. However these higher primates may differ in their protestations, they are at one in their zest for killing off all other forms of life, and their own kind.

This topic does not merit verse, except the briefest confessional query:

> Are you
> a yahoo
> too?

Guy Butler

Since going to press, Professor Michael Roberts has drawn my attention to the devastating criticism of Dr von Sonnenschein's hypothesis contained in the Ph.D. thesis (Tom Jones University) of Professor Snyde Krutchenkikker. Krutchenkikker damns Sonnenschein's attempted exculpation of *Homo Sapiens* at the expense of the Yahoos as a typical middle class ploy to blacken the masses. According to Krutchenkikker, Dr Lemuel Gulliver's account of the Yahoos is a classic example of the bourgeois ability to create mythical creatures on to whom they can project their guilty abhorrence of the unwashed poor. As for Sonnenschien's concern for the extinct Quagga, Krutchenkikker appears to be an unqualified Darwinian. A yahoo with a rifle ('all power comes through the barrel of a gun') is clearly fitter to survive than any form of life without one.

ZEBRA *Zebras are divided into three distinct species and are members of the horse family.*

NAMES
English: *zebra*
Afrikaans: *sebra*
African: *idube (Z), pitsi (N-S)*

DISTRIBUTION: Zebras are found only in Africa. They inhabit plains and lightly wooded savannahs and in the case of mountain zebras, mountainous areas. Grevy's Zebra is found only north of the equator; Burchell's Zebra is the most numerous and widely distributed - from the Eastern Transvaal northwards in most of East Africa; the Mountain Zebras are restricted to small areas in the Cape and in Namibia and southern Angola.

DIET: Predominantly grazers but will on occasion browse from bushes and trees. They must drink regularly.

FEATURES AND HABITS: Prominent black stripes on a whitish background are their most distinctive feature. The stripe patterns vary between species. Mountain Zebras are pure white on the undersides of their bodies whereas the Burchell's have stripes which go all around the torso. The markings of an individual animal is as peculiar to him as is a fingerprint to a human being. Grevy's Zebra is the largest species and the Cape Mountain Zebra the smallest. Zebras are gregarious and found in herds of varying size. They are also often found in association with antelopes such as impala and wildebeest and sometimes even ostriches. They are easily caught by larger predators but lead stallions often defend their groups courageously and mares will do everything possible to defend their foals. Zebras are noisy, restless animals and have a distinctive barking whinny which sounds a lot like Kwa-ha, the onomatopoeic name given them by the San and Khoi people. Rival stallions fight violently and much kicking and biting goes on. One foal is dropped at any time throughout the year but foaling peaks in summer. In the past zebra were killed in their thousands for their skins and meat. The colonists were not too keen on 'horse-meat' but gave it to their servants. This no doubt accounts for the disappearance of the Quagga.

THE ZEBRAS

From the dark woods that breathe of fallen showers,
Harnessed with level rays in golden reins,
The zebras draw the dawn across the plains
Wading knee-deep among the scarlet flowers.
The sunlight, zithering their flanks with fire,
Flashes between the shadows as they pass
Barred with electric tremor through the grass
Like wind along the gold strings of a lyre.

Into the flushed air snorting rosy plumes
That smoulder round their feet in drifting fumes,
With dove-like voices call the distant fillies,
While round the herds the stallion wheels his flight,
Engine of beauty volted with delight,
To roll his mare among the trampled lilies.

Roy Campbell

ZEBRA

Where the grass spikes lank and
loamless, where the wind
scoops earth and thankless
pennypinching water-holes
nastily eye the sky
through brass-green lenses
they run striped and breezy
uprooting showery tufts
with uplifted yellow teeth;
rebellious they are, unbridled.

Destructive, most of them
claw-stained, they have been
fenced into freedom.

Their whippy tails are burr-stuck
and hooves are wreathed in dung;
convict-flanked they gallop
through the thorn lists of liberty,
soulless and without humour,
as if they know
as if they made it so
this meat is rancid.

Douglas Livingstone

from THE CLAN PRAISES OF THE PEOPLE OF CHIHOTA'S CLAN

... A service has been rendered, Zebra.
Kindly done, Striped one;
   One who yearns to share;
   Hornless beast from Renje.
Thank you, Tembo;
   Adorned with your own stripes;
   Iridescent and glittering creatures;
   Whose skin is soft as girls' is;
   One on which the eye dwells all day, as on the solitary
      cow of a poor man;
   Creature that makes the forests beautiful;
   Weaver of lines;
   Who wear your skin for display,
   Drawn with lines so clearly defined;
   You who thread beads in patterns;
   Dappled fish;
   Hatching round the neck of a pot,
   Beauty spots cut to rise in a crescent on the forehead;
   A patterned belt for the waist;
   Light reflected;
   Dazzling the eyes.
It is its own instinct, the Zebra's,
   adorned as if with strings of beads around the waist
      as women are;
   Wild creature without anger or any grudge;
   Lineage with a totem that is nowhere a stranger;
   Line that stretches everywhere;
   Owners of the land.
A service has been rendered, Big Muzzle,
Yes, rendered, Proud Mane ...

Shona, Recorded by A.C. Hodza

ZEBRA

Zebra has electric hair
striped in black and white

generates a striking kick
integration on the hoof

blowing off like dynamite
holding more than he can bare

there's a stallion there's a mare
foaling how they breed

overblown it makes you sick
how they sow their stripy seed

powerhouse you stay aloof
Zebra Zebra gallop east

west north especially south
suck the air in with your mouth

we need your type to settle here
to crop the grass at least.

Stephen Gray

Another story of the zebra is that it fought with the baboon for access
to a waterhole. During the struggle the zebra fell into the baboon's fire
which was burning close by. This had two effects. The first was to
pain the zebra into renewed vigour so that it threw the baboon up into
the rocks at the top of a nearby hill, where it has remined ever since.
The second effect was to burn the stripes into the skin of the zebra.
(Thomas, 1950)

Woodhouse

Biographical Notes on Authors

ADAMS, Peter Robert Charles (pen-name Perseus)
Born in Cape Town, 1933. University of Cape Town. Teacher of English, poet and short-story writer. In 1953 hitch-hiked through Africa to England. Served a prison sentence in Wormwood Scrubbs, for stowing away. Taught in Cape Town until 1965, when he travelled to the Far East. Lived in Hong Kong for eighteen months, and on the Greek Islands for periods in 1966, 1971 and 1972. Contributed verse to numerous South African literary periodicals and anthologies. Awards: The South African Poetry Prize 1963; Eastern Province Poetry Prize 1964; Festival of Rhodesia Poetry Prize 1970; 2nd prize in The John Keats Memorial Prize, London 1971.
  The Land at my Door, Cape Town: Human and Rousseau, 1965.
  Grass for the Unicorn, Cape Town: Juta, 1975.

AWOONOR, Kofi
The son of a Sierra Leonean father and a Togolese mother, Kofi Awoonor (who started writing under the name George Awoonor-Williams) was born in 1935 in Wheta in the Keta district of Ghana. Educated at the Achimoto Secondary School, and the universities of Ghana, London and California, he later joined the staff of the State University of New York, where he instituted a course of African literature. He established his literary reputation with the poetry volume *Rediscovery and other poems* (1964) and has since published widely, including a novel *This Earth, my Brother* (1971), and, together with Adali-Mortty, edited an anthology of Ghanian poetry called *Messages: Poems from Ghana* (1970)

BELLOC, Hilaire (1870-1953)
A versatile British writer and Catholic propagandist, now chiefly recalled for his light verse, as in *Cautionary Tales* and *A Bad Child's Book of Beasts.*
  Complete Verse, London: Duckworth, 1970.

BRETTELL, Noel Harry
Born in Lye, Worcestershire, 1908. University of Birmingham. Went to Rhodesia in 1930, and became headmaster of rural schools in remote regions. His poem 'Mantis and Moth' was placed as runner-up in the 1972 Best Poem of the Year Competition, run by the English Association of Britain. Recipient of 1972 PEN Literary Award, and the Book Centre of Rhodesia Literary Award 1973. Has had poems published in South African and Zimbabwean anthologies and magazines. Retired and living in Kadoma, Zimbabwe.
  A Rhodesian Leave, (privately published).
  Bronze Frieze, Oxford University Press, 1950.
  Season and Pretext, Salisbury: Poetry Society of Rhodesia, 1977.

BUTLER, David
Son of Frederick Guy Butler is a teacher of English, presently attached to a Black Adult Educational project in Grahamstown.

BUTLER, Frederick Guy
Born in Cradock, 1918. Studied at Rhodes University and later at Oxford University. After war service, he lectured at the University of the Witwatersrand and at Rhodes University,

where he was Professor of English from 1952 until his retirement in 1987. Butler has written plays and five volumes of poetry, and edited several anthologies of verse. His *Selected Poems* was awarded the C.N.A. Prize for Literature in 1975. His main interests are Shakespeare and S A Literature. He was awarded honorary doctorates by the University of Natal (1970), and the University of the Witwatersrand (1985).

Selected Poems, Johannesburg: Donker, 1975.

CAMPBELL, Ignatius Royston Dunnachie (Roy) (1901-1957)
Born in Durban and studied briefly at Oxford. After his return to South Africa in 1926 he edited the literary periodical *Voorslag* with William Plomer and Laurens van der Post. He lived in Europe for most of his life and published eight volumes of poetry including translations from French, Spanish and Portuguese poetry. The best- known South African poet in English.

Collected Works, Johannesburg: Donker, 1985

CARROLL, Lewis (1832-1898)
A British mathematician, best known as a writer of the children's books, *Alice in Wonderland* (1865) and *Through the Looking Glass* (1872) - which mark an epoch in the history of dream literature. He was also a master of nonsense verse.

CHIMSORO, Samuel
Born 1949, Murewa, Zimbabwe. Fletcher High School and Harare polytechnic. Laboratory technician at University of Zimbabwe. Poems widely anthologised in Zimbabwe. Now technician with Ministry of Energy and Water Resources.

Smoke and Flames, Harare: Mambo Press 1978
Nothing is impossible, 1983

CILLIERS, Charl Jean Francois
Born in Cape Town, 1941. Educated in Pretoria. His poetry first appeared in *New Coin*, and he has subsequently published three collections. By profession he is a translator at the House of Assembly, Cape Town.

West-Falling Light, Cape Town: Tafelberg, 1971.
Has Winter No Wisdom, Cape Town: Maskew Miller, 1978.

CLOUTS, Sydney David (1926-1982)
Born in Cape Town. University of Cape Town and Rhodes University, Grahamstown. Research Fellow, Institute for the Study of English in Africa, 1969. Contributed widely to South African and English literary periodicals and anthologies. Awarded the Ingrid Jonker Prize, and the Olive Schreiner award 1968. Died in London.

One Life, Cape Town: Purnell, 1966
Collected Poems, Cape Town: David Philip, 1984.

CULLINAN, Patrick Roland has also used the pen-name Patrick Roland
Born in Pretoria, 1932. Poet and Novelist; in 1974 co-founder with Lionel Abrahams, of Bateleur Press; 1980 editor of *The Bloody Horse*. He was awarded, with Christopher van Wyk, the 1980 Olive Schreiner Prize. Lecturer in English, University of the Western Cape.

Today is not Different, Cape Town: David Philip, Mantis Poets, 1978.
White Hail in the Orchard, Cape Town: David Philip, 1984.

DE GRAFT, Joe (1924-1978)
Born in Ghana in 1924, de Graft was educated at the University College of the Gold Coast.
He instituted the theatre arts programme for the School of Music and Drama at the University of Ghana, and later travelled to Nairobi where he taught drama at the University of Nairobi. His plays include *Sons and Daughters* (1963) and *Visitors from the Past,* later revised as *Through a Film Darkly* (1970). His poetry was included in *Messages: Poems from Ghana,* a 1970 anthology selected by Awoonor and Adali-Mortty, and a collection of his own work appeared as *Beneath the Jazz and Brass* (1975). He died in 1978 not long after returning to Ghana from Kenya.

DEDERICK, Robert
Born in England, 1919. Settled in South Africa in 1951. Retired solicitor and legal adviser; freelance broadcaster and sports journalist on the *Cape Argus*. Won the 1967 State Poetry Prize, and the 1971 Pringle award.
   The Quest and Other Poems, Cape Town: Purnell, 1968.
   Bi-focal, Cape Town: David Philip, 1974.

DELIUS, Anthony Roland St Martin
Born in Simonstown, 1916. Studied at Rhodes University and saw war service in the SA Intelligence Corps. He has been a journalist since 1947. He now lives in London, broadcasts on the BBC and writes poetry and short stories; his novel *Border* won the CNA Literary Award in 1976. His published poetry includes:
   The unknown border, Cape Town: Balkema, 1954.
   The last division, Cape Town: Human & Rousseau, 1959.
   A corner of the world, Cape Town: Human & Rousseau, 1962.
   Black south easter, Grahamstown: *New Coin,* ISEA, 1966.

EGLINGTON, Charles Beaumont (1918-1970)
Born in Johannesburg, 1918. University of the Witwatersrand. Served in North Africa and Italy in World War II. Worked on various South African newspapers until 1962, when he bacame editor of *Optima,* the quarterly journal of a mining corporation. Poet, art-critic, broadcaster and translator. Contributed poems to South African literary journals and anthologies. He also translated from Afrikaans (two novels by Etienne Leroux) and Portuguese. Unpublished manuscript *A Lap Full of Seed,* 1967. Died suddenly in 1970.
   Under the Horizon, Cape Town: Purnell, 1977.

ELIOT Thomas Stearns (1888-1965)
American who adopted British Nationality. Enormously influential poet e.g. *The Waste Land* (1922), *Four Quartets* (1935-42); critic: e.g.*The Sacred Word* (1920), *Selected Essays* (1932); and dramatist e.g. *Murder in the Cathedral* (1935). 'The Hippopotamus' predates his conversion to Christianity (1927). His feeling for animals emerges most notably in *Uncle Tom's Book of Practical Cats.*
   Collected Poems 1909-1962, London: Faber, 1963.

FAIRBRIDGE, Kingsley Ogilvie (1885-1924)
Born in Grahamstown. He left school at the age of 11 and moved to Zimbabwe where his father was a surveyor. He encouraged the emigration of poor children to Britain's colonies, and established farm schools in Australia for that purpose.
   Veld Verse and Other Lines, Oxford University Press, 1928.

FARMER, Harold
Born 1943, Windhoek, Namibia. Educated Rhodes University and the University of Cape Town. Has lived in South Africa, India, Zambia, and Zimbabwe. Practised law for six years. Lecturer in English at University of Zimbabwe. Poems have appeared in *New Coin, Two Tone, Rhodesian Poetry Review, Sewanee Review, Ariel, Meanjin, Poetry Australia* and *World Poetry*.

FORTUNE, George
Born 1915, Bulawayo. School of Oriental and African Studies, University of London, and the School of African Studies, University of Cape Town. Professional studies in the Society of Jesus. Held chair of African Languages at University of Zimbabwe from 1960 until his retirement. Lectured at Seke Teachers' College until appointed in 1984 to institute Shona courses at UNISA. Has published widely on Shona language and literature, notably *Shona Praise Poetry* (with Dr Aaron C. Hodza) (1979). Has also done considerable research in Ndebele and is compiling a dictionary and grammar in this language.

GILFILLAN, Berin N.
Born in Johannesburg, 1961. While at Hilton College he wrote 'The Tortoise and the Hare', which was published in 1979 in *English Alive*. B.A. in Communications from the University of Michigan; M.A., CBN, Virginia Beach. At present a Television Director/Producer for Christ for All Nations, Frankfurt. Visited 11 African countries in 1986.

GRAY, Stephen
Born in Cape Town, 1941. Novelist and poet. Cambridge and Iowa State Universities. Professor in English at Rand Afrikaans University, Johannesburg. Was joint-editor of *Izwi* magazine. Poems published in numerous periodicals. Author of two published novels. Editor of several anthologies of South African verse and prose.
   The Assassination of Shaka, text by Stephen Gray; 43 woodcuts by
       Cecil Skotnes, Johannesburg: McGraw-Hill, 1974.
   It's about Time, Cape Town: David Philip, 1974.
   Hottentot Venus & other poems, Cape Town: David Philip, 1979.

GREIG, Robert
Born in Johannesburg, 1948. University of the Witwatersrand. Travelled in Europe and southern Africa. Worked as feature-writer and reviewer on the *Cape Times*. Won the *Pringle Award* in 1976 for book and play reviews, and the *Olive Schreiner Prize* for his volume of poetry, *Talking Bull* in 1977. Now works as drama critic for *The Star* in Johannesburg.
   Talking Bull, Johannesburg: Bateleur Press, 1975.

GUITERMAN, Arthur (1871-1943)
American poet and journalist, best known for his humorous verse.

HAMUTYINEI, Mordikai A.
Born 1934, Gutu, Zimbabwe. School teacher. Political detainee and studied 'O' Level during this time. Later joined Mambo Press and did in-service training as editor and journalist. Now teaching at Mupamombe Secondary School, Gutu. Poems have appeared in Shona anthologies since 1970 including *Nhetembo* and *Mabvimira Enhetembo*. His poems have been translated into English by the poet himself, by Professor George Fortune and by the Zimbabwe Literature Bureau. Author of eight Shona novels.

HEWETT, Bruce William Dixie
Born in Cape Town, 1939. Educated at the Diocesan College. His poetry has been published in *New Coin*, as well as in privately published collections. He was awarded the English Academy's Thomas Pringle Prize for Poetry in 1978.
The Dawn of Song, Grahamstown: *New Coin*, ISEA, 1985.

HEYWOOD, Terrence
Born in Johannesburg, of New Zealand parents; educated P.T.P.S., Johannesburg; Malvern College; Worcester College, Oxford (MA), and a short period at Uppsala University, Sweden. Since the age of fourteen his visits to South Africa have been infrequent. Has been a free-lance writer, and also engaged in forestry. At present with Association of Special Libraries and Information Bureaux.
How Smoke Gets into the Air, London: Fortune Press, 1951.
Architectonic, London: Fortune Press, 1953.

HODZA, Aaron C. (1924-1983)
Born 1924, Mazowe, Zimbabwe. Since 1964 with Department of African Languages, University of Zimbabwe. Translator and linguist. Assisted in the compilation of many Shona grammar texts. Honorary President of the Shona Society. Poems, and articles on Shona history, legend, and literature, published in journals in South Africa and Zimbabwe. Poems broadcast on ZBC. Acknowledged authority on Shona linguistics and literature. Published, *Ngano Dzamatambidzanwa: Traditional Shona folk tales*.
Shona Praise Poetry (with George Fortune) 1979.

HOVE, Chenjerai
Born 1954, Mazvihwa, Zvishavane, Zimbabwe. Gweru Teachers' College, and BA Unisa. Editor with Mambo Press for four years. Now editor with Zimbabwe Publishing House. Poems in Zimbabwean journals and anthologies, including *And Now the Poets Speak: Poems Inspired by the Struggle for Zimbabwe* (1981). Co-author of *Swimming in Floods of Tears* (1983) (with Lyamba wa Kabika).
Up in Arms, 1982
Red Hills of Home, Harare: Mambo Press, 1985.

KARIARA, Jonathan
Born in the Nyeri District of Kenya in 1935, Jonathan Kariara was educated localy and subsequently studied English at the Makerere University College, Kampala, Uganda. He worked for some time on the staff of the East African Literature Bureau in Nairobi before taking up the post of editor with Oxford University Press. He has travelled widely in West Africa and Europe and his short stories and poems have been published in several major anthologies.

KEECH, Roy
Born in England, 1919. First came to South Africa after service in the Indian Army during the World War II. He married his wife, Ruth, a highly regarded South African poet in her own right, during a further stretch in the Colonial Service, and returned to South Africa in 1953. His poetry has been published in *New Coin* and *Bolt*.

KUNENE, Daniel P.
He was born in Edenville, near Kroonstad, and spent the early years of his life there. After obtaining his first degree in 1949, he went on to do post-graduate work at the University of Cape Town, where he received his Ph.D in 1961. He left South Africa and is currently

Professor of African Languages and Literature at the University of Wisconsin at Madison. Apart from various critical works he has published a collection of short stories, *From the Pit of Hell to the Spring of Life* (1986) as well as two volumes of poetry, *Pirates have become our kings* (1979), and *A Seed must seem to die* (1981)

LETTY, Cythna (Forssman, Dr Cythna Lindenberg) (1895-1985)
Born in Standerton, Transvaal, and worked for most of her life at the Botanical Research Institute in Pretoria. She was regarded as one of South Africa's greatest botanical artists, but was first recognized as a poet late in her career when a selection of her poetry was published in *Lantern*. A volume of her verse with some of her later drawings was published in 1981. Honours conferred on her include the Grenfell medal of the Royal Horticultural Society and an honorary Doctorate of Laws from the University of the Witwatersrand.
    Children of the Hours, Johannesburg: Donker, 1981.

LEIPOLDT, Christian Frederick Louis (1880-1947)
Born in Worcester, Cape, and educated by his father, a minister, in Clanwilliam. His poetry was one of the inspirations of the defeated Afrikaners after the Boer War, in which he had served as a war correspondent. He studied medicine in London, travelled in Europe and America, and became a school medical inspector in the Transvaal and then the Cape. From 1925 he practised as a paediatrician in Cape Town. He wrote poetry in English - *The Ballad of Dick King and other poems*, 1949 - but is best known as an Afrikaans poet. He wrote eight volumes of poetry.
    Versamelde gedigte, Cape Town: Tafelberg, 1980.

LEWIS, Clive Staples (1898-1963)
Scholar, critic, novelist, poet. Best known for popular religious writings such as *The Screwtape Letters* (1940), science fiction novels, and stories for children.

LIVINGSTONE, Douglas James
Born in Kuala Lumpur, Malaysia, 1932. Educated in Natal and Zimbabwe. He works as a bacteriologist in Natal. In 1965 he received the Guinness Poetry Award, and in 1970 the Cholmondeley Prize for Poetry and in 1975 the Olive Schreiner Prize for a play. He has published several volumes of poetry.
    Eyes Closed against the Sun, London: Oxford University Press, 1970.
    Selected Poems, Johannesburg: Donker, 1984.
    Sjambok and other poems from Africa, Johannesburg: Donker 1988.

LOUW, N. P. van Wyk (1906-1970)
Born in Sutherland in the Karoo, 1906. He lectured at the University of Cape Town and in Amsterdam until he became Professor of Afrikaans and Nederlands at the University of the Witwatersrand in 1958. *Raka* (1941) was the first epic poem published in Afrikaans. He also wrote poetic dramas, such as *Dias* (1951) and *Germanicus*. He is regarded by many as the greatest poet of his language.
    Versamelde Gedigte, Cape Town: Tafelberg, 1981.

MACNAB, Roy Martin
Born in Durban, 1923. Poet and historian. He studied at Oxford and served as a journalist and as a member of the diplomatic corps before becoming the London Director of the South African Foundation from 1968 until his retirement in 1984. Lives in southern France.
    Poems by Roy MacNab & Douglas Reid Skinner, Cape Town: David Philip, 1981.

MARKOWITZ, Arthur
Arthur Markowitz has published two novels, *Facing North* (1949) and *Market Street* (1959), and a book on the wild life in South African game reserves. Apart from these, *With Uplifted Tongue: stories, myths and fables of the South African Bushmen told in their manner* (1956) with an introduction by Professor Phillip Tobias, was followed by *The Rebirth of the Ostrich* (1971) published by the National Museum and Art Gallery in Gaborone, Botswana.

MANDISHONA, A. G.
Born 1940, Makwiro, Zimbabwe. B. Sc. University of Zimbabwe. Artist. Shona author and poet. Poems in Zimbabwean journals and anthologies.

MILLER, Ruth (1919-1969)
Born in Uitenhage, Cape Province. Taught English at St Mary's Convent, Johannesburg, until the end of 1965. Poems published in journals in South Africa, Britain and the United States and included in the anthology, *War Poems of the United Nations* (1943). First book of verse, *Floating Island*, won the Ingrid Jonker Prize for Poetry in 1966.
   Floating Island, Cape Town: Human & Rousseau, 1965.
   Selected Poems, London: Chatto and Windus, 1968.

MOLONY, Rowland
Born in Harrietsham, Kent, 1946. He spent five years in the Royal Air Force, followed by four years at Ulster and Exeter Universities. In 1975 he emigrated to Zimbabwe to take up a teaching post in Bulawayo. His work has appeared in a number of poetry magazines, and a selection of his poetry was published together with the work of three other Zimbabwean poets in *Four Voices: Poetry from Zimbabwe* (1982). Now lives in Britain.

MTSHALI, Oswald Mbuyiseni
Born in Vryheid, Natal, 1940. He went to school in Natal and then moved to Johannesburg where he worked as a teacher in Soweto. He has contributed poetry to magazines and newspapers and in 1975 won the Olive Schreiner prize for English literature.
   Sounds of a cowhide drum, Johannesburg: Donker, 1982.
   Fireflames, Pietermaritzburg, Shuter & Shooter, 1980.

NASH, Ogden (1902-1971)
American poet; master of light, sardonic verse - twelve volumes between 1931 and 1957.
   Verses from 1929 On, London: Dent, 1961.

OPPERMAN, Diederik Johannes (1914-1986)
Afrikaans poet, born in the district of Dundee in Natal. He went to school in Natal and taught in Pietermaritzburg and Johannesburg. He served on the editorial staff of *Die Huisgenoot* before lecturing at the University of Cape Town. From 1960 until his death he was Professor of Afrikaans at the University of Stellenbosch. Opperman has published verse dramas, criticism, and nine volumes of poetry in Afrikaans.
   Nege ster oor Nineve, Cape Town: Nasionale Boekhandel, 1958.
   Naaldekoker, Cape Town: Tafelberg, 1974.

PLOMER, William Charles Franklyn (1903-1973)
Born in Pietersburg. He was a farmer in the Eastern Cape and a trader in Zululand, and edited a literary magazine, *Voorslag*, with Roy Campbell. After the publication of his satirical novel *Turbott Wolfe* (1926) he left South Africa for Japan and later settled in England,

where he worked as an adviser to a London publisher. Before his death in 1973, he wrote novels, short stories, poetry, a biography of Cecil John Rhodes, two auto-biographies and the libretti of four operas by Benjamin Britten.

Collected Poems, London: Cape, 1960.

POUND, Ezra (1885-1972)
American poet who exerted a great influence on English poetry, particularly on T S Eliot. Like Eliot he attempted to see European culture as a whole, not fragmented into many national cultures. He spent many of his later years on a long poem *Cantos*, from which this extract is taken.

Seventy Cantos, London Faber, 1950.

PRICE, Herbert (1858-1936)
Born near Queenstown where he was in business for many years. His poetry featured prominently in many early anthologies, and he published one volume.

Poems and Sonnets, Queenstown: Welch, 1914.

PRINGLE, Thomas (1789-1834)
Born in Scotland and came to South Africa as an 1820 settler after studying at Edinburgh University. After a spell on the frontier he worked as a government librarian in Cape Town. In opposing Lord Charles Somerset's attempt to close down his *South African Journal,* Pringle established the principle of press freedom. In 1826 he returned to England where he served as secretary to the Anti-Slavery Society.

Poems Illustrative of South Africa, Cape Town: Struik, 1970.

RICHARDS, Laura Elizabeth (1850-1943)
Prolific American novelist, short story writer and poet, best known for her stories for children.

SLATER, Francis Carey (1876-1958)
Born at Umjilo near Alice. He had only a little over two years of formal education, at Lovedale, and spend his working life as a banker in various towns in the Eastern Cape and Transkei, finally retiring as general manager of the Standard Bank in Grahamstown. Slater published three works of fiction and an autobiography, *Settlers' Heritage* (1954), and he championed the cause of South African poetry in two anthologies. He published eight volumes of his own poetry.

Collected Poems, Edinburgh: Blackwood, 1957.

STOCKENSTRÖM, Wilma
Born in 1933. Afrikaans poet and novelist, notable for the suggestive power and penetration of her symbols. She is also an actress of distinction.

Van Vergetelheid en van Glans. Cape Town: Human & Rousseau, 1976.
Monster verse, Cape Town: Human & Rousseau, 1984.

STRAUSS, Peter Erik
Born in Pietermaritzburg, 1941. University of Natal and University of Cambridge. Has travelled in Europe, and spent several years in England and Germany. Lecturer in English at the University of Natal. Leading critic and co-editor of the literary journal *Donga*. His poetry has been published in South African periodicals *Theoria* and *Thalia* (University of Natal journal), as well as Cambridge journals *Delta* and *Griffin*.

Photographs of Bushmen, Johannesburg: Bateleur Press, 1974.
Bishop Bernward's door & other poems, Cape Town: David Philip, 1983.

STYLE, Colin Thomas Elliot
Born 1937, Harare. Rhodes University. Worked for a number of years in Market Research in Africa, and then as an Export Marketing Research Adviser with British Overseas Trade Board. University poetry prize. Poems widely anthologised and published in journals in UK, USA, Australia, Canada, South Africa, and Zimbabwe. Co-editor of literary journal, *Chirimo*, and co-producer first-ever LP disc of readings of Zimbabwean poets. Critical articles also widely published. Book reviewer on BBC. Wrote and compiled a programme, 'Dream of Ophir', for BBC Radio 3, on Zimbabwean literature. Co-editor with O-lan Style *Mambo Book of Zimbabwean Verse in English* (1986). *Baobab Street (1977)* won the Ingrid Jonker Prize for best published collection in English in southern Africa. Now living and writing in Kent.
   Baobab Street Johannesburg: Bateleur Press, 1977.
   Musical Saw, Mopani Series, 1981.

THESEN, Hjalmar Peter
Born in Knysna, 1925. Educated at St. Andrews College, Grahamstown and the University of Cape Town. He has produced four novels, the most recent of which was *A Deadly Presence*, published in 1982, and a collection of newspaper articles written originally as fortnightly columns in the Eastern Province Herald.
   Poems, Box 10, Knysna.

'TOTIUS' (Du Toit, Jacob Daniel) (1877-1953)
Afrikaans poet, scholar, translator of the Bible, and professor of theology; a patriot and great champion of the Afrikaans language. Collected works comprise 8 volumes.
   Vyftig gedigte van Totius, Cape Town: Tafelberg, 1976.

VAN HEERDEN, Ernst
Born in Pearston, Eastern Cape, 1916. Educated at the local school and Grey High School, Port Elizabeth. He studied at the Universities of Stellenbosch and Amsterdam, and after further study in the United States, he returned to lecture at the University of the Witwatersrand where he became Professor of Afrikaans and Nederlands in 1970. In addition to his poetry, for which he won the Hertzog Prize in 1962 and the Hofmeyr Prize in 1975, and some of which he has translated into English, he has also written extensively in the field of literary criticism. Honorary Doctorates have been awarded to him by the University of the Witwatersrand (1982) and Rhodes University (1985).
   Kleur van Donkerte: verse 1924-1976, Cape Town: Human & Rousseau, 1981.

WRIGHT, David John Murray
Born in Johannesburg, 1920. Left South Africa in 1934. Educated Northampton School for the Deaf and Oriel College, Oxford. Has published eight volumes of poetry, edited seven anthologies, and translated *Beowulf* and *The Canterbury Tales*.
   Selected Poems, Johannesburg: Donker, 1980.

WYNDHAM, George (1863-1913)
English politician and man of letters. - 'a bold rider to hounds, a letter writer of the first rank; he abhorred blatant women, pompous bores, and the foolish interrupter'. D.N.B.

YATES, Anne
Born in Johannesburg, 1922. University of the Witwatersrand and Somerville College, Oxford. Sometime lecturer in Economics, University of the Witwatersrand. Poems in various anthologies and periodicals including *A Book of South African Verse*, *New Coin* and *Contrast*. Now lives in Oxford.
Uneven World: Poems, London: Hand and Flower Press, 1958.
Set in Brightness, Cape Town: Purnell, 1968.

ZIMUNYA, Musaemura B.
Born 1949, Mutare, Zimbabwe. Goromonzi High School and university of Kent, UK. Lecturer in English at University of Zimbabwe. A number of verse collections published: *Zimbabwe Ruins* (bound with D.E. Borrell in a Double Volume in the Mopani Poets Series) (1981); *Thought Tracks* (1982); *Kingfisher, Jikinya and Other Poems* (1983); *Country Dawns and City Lights* (1985). Also a criticism of Zimbabwean fiction, *Those Years of Drought and Hunger* (1982). Co-editor (with Mudereri Kadhani) of *And Now the poets Speak: Poems Inspired by the Struggle for Zimbabwe* (1981); Edited *Chakarira Chindunduma: Shona Poems Inspired by the Struggle for Zimbabwe* (1986).

ZVOBGO, Eddison J.
Born 1935, Mtilikwa, Zimbabwe. Roma University, Lesotho, and Taft University, USA. Initially in teaching. Long period in detention during which he completed LL.B. with University of London. Writes poetry in Shona and English with poems in journals and anthologies in USA and Zimbabwe. Cabinet Minister.

Sources of Poems

GENERAL - THE LANDSCAPE
From *The Flaming Terrapin*. Roy Campbell, *Collected Works,* Johannesburg: Donker, 1985.
'Afar in the Desert'. Thomas Pringle, *Afar in the Desert & other South African Poems*, London: Longmans, 1881.
'Silence Allowed. Msinga Mjusi Five Thirty'. Roy Keech.
'A Bamboo Day' Douglas Livingstone, *Selected Poems*, Johannesburg: Donker, 1984.
'The Floating Island'. Ruth Miller from *Floating Island,* Cape Town: Human & Rousseau, 1965.
'Animal Kingdom'. Sydney Clouts, *Collected Poems,* Cape Town: David Philip, 1984.
Extract from 'A Voyage to Africa. David Wright, *Selected Poems,* Johannesburg: Donker, 1980.

Animals in Alphabet

The following pages also serve as acknowledgements to the poets and the publishers who kindly granted their permission to include poems in this anthology.

ANTS   EXTRACT from Canto LXXXI Ezra Pound, *The Cantos,* New York: New Directions, 1948
THE ANT Ogden Nash, *Collected Verse from 1929 on.* London: Dent, 1961
BY AN ANTHEAP (Terence Heywood, *A Book of S.A. Verse,* selected and introduced by Guy Butler, London: O.U.P., 1958)
TO COME BACK HOME (S. Chimsoro, *Smoke and Flames,* Harare: Mambo Press, 1978)
TO YOU, ANT (A.G. Mandishona, *The Mambop Book of Zimbabwean Verse in English*, Harare: Mambo Press, 1986)

ANTBEAR   ANTBEAR (N.H. Brettell, *Season and Pretext Poems:* The Poetry Society of Rhodesia 1977)

BABOON   BONGWI (Kingsley Fairbridge, *Veld Verse,* O.U.P. 1928)
The Theology of Bongwi, the Baboon. (Roy Campbell, *Collected Works,* Johannesburg: Donker, 1985)

BUFFALO   BUFFALO (Charles Eglington, *Under the Horizon,* Purnell, 1977)
THE BUFFALO (Herbert Price, *The New Centenary Book of S.A. Verse,* ed. F.C. Slater. London: Longmans, 1945)
LONE BULL (Charl Cilliers, New Coin Poetry, October, 1966, Vol.2, No.3)

CHAMELEON AT A SNAIL'S PACE PLEASE (Oswald Mtshali, *Sounds of a Cowhide Drum,* Johannesburg: Donker, 1982)
CHAMELEON (Anthony Delius, *A Book of S.A. Verse,* Ed. Guy Butler. London: O.U.P., 1958)
UNDER THE DRIPPING TREES (Rowland Molony, *Four Voices: Poetry from Zimbabwe,* Bulawayo: Books of Zimbabwe, 1982)

CHEETAH   CHEETAH (Charles Eglington, *A Book of S.A. Verse,* Ed. Guy Butler. London: O.U.P., 1958)

COBRA   SALUTE (Sydney Clouts, *Collected Poems,* Cape Town: David Philip, 1984)
DIE KOPERKAPEL (Louis Leipoldt, Trans. Guy Butler in *Afrikaans Poetry with English Translations,* Cape Town: O.U.P., 1962)
ADONIS (Rowland Molony, *Four Voices : Poetry from Zimbabwe,* Bulawayo: Books of Zimbabwe, 1982)

CROCODILE HOW DOTH - (Lewis Carroll, *An Anthology of Animal Poetry,* Ed. K.A. Mason, Pelican Books, 1940)
CROCODILE (R. Molony, c/o New Coin Poetry, I.S.E.A., Rhodes University, Grahamstown)
THE CROCODILE (Bruce Hewett, *The Dawn of Song,* Grahamstown: New Coin, I.S.E.A., 1985)

DRAGON-FLY DRAGON-FLY LOVE (William Plomer, *Collected Poems,* London: Cape, 1960)

DUIKER	A PIECE OF EARTH (Douglas Livingstone, *The Anvil's Undertone*, Johannesburg: Donker, 1978
	DUIKER DOE (N.H. Brettell, *Season and Pretext*, The Poetry Society of Rhodesia, P.O. Box A70, Avondale, Harare, Zimbabwe)
EAGLE	BLACK EAGLE (Charles Eglington, *Under The Horizon*, Cape Town: Purnell, 1977)
	EAGLE (N.P. van Wyk Louw. Trans. Guy Butler, *Afrikaans Poems with English Translations*, Cape Town: O.U.P., 1962)
	THE EAGLE AND THE SKY DIVER (Bruce Hewett, *The Dawn of Song*, Grahamstown: New Coin, I.S.E.A, 1985)
ELAND	THE ELAND (Wilma Stokenström, *Van Vergetelheid en Glans*, Cape Town: Human & Rousseau, 1976. Trans. Guy Butler, 122 High Street, Grahamstown)
ELEPHANT	ELEPHANT (N.H. Bretell, *Season and Pretext Poems*, Harare: Poetry Society of Rhodesia, 1977)
	ELETELEPHONY (Laura Richards, *Tirra Lirra*, Little Brown, 1932 - from *The Children's Book of Comic Verse*, Ed. C.Logue. Pan Books, 1980)
	ELEPHANT HUNT (Hjalmar Thesen, *Poems*, Box 10, Knysna)
	TO A DEAD ELEPHANT (Douglas Livingstone, *Selected Poems*, Johannesburg: Donker, 1984)
	WRITTEN IN AN ELEPHANT'S GRAVEYARD (Bruce Hewett, *The Dawn of Song*, New Coin, I.S.E.A., Rhodes University Grahamstown, 1985)
FROG	TO SEPARATE THE TADPOLES FROM THE FROGS (Bruce Hewett, *Dawn of Song*, Grahamstown: New Coin, 1985, I.S.E.A.)
	FROG (For Ruth Harnett) Sydney Clouts, *Collected Poems*, Cape Town: David Philip, 1984.)
	THE FROG (Anonymous)
	FROGS (D.J. Opperman, Trans. Jean Branford, *Afrikaans Poems with English Translations*, Cape Town: O.U.P., 1962)
	FROGS (Rowland Molony, *Four Voices : Poetry from Zimbabwe*, Bulawayo: Books of Zimbabwe, 1982)
GIRAFFE	FROM DREAMING SPIRES (Roy Campbell, *(Collected Works*, Johannesburg: Donker, 1985)
	CONVERSATION WITH A GIRAFFE AT DUSK IN THE ZOO (Douglas Livingstone *Selected Poems*, Johannesburg: Donker, 1984)
	GIRAFFES (N.H. Brettell, *Season and Pretext Poems*, Harare: Poetry Society of Rhodesia, 1977)
	GROOM, GIRAFFE, EMPEROR (Guy Butler, 122 High Street, Grahamstown)
	THE GIRAFFE (George Wyndham, in *The Children's Book of Comic Verse*, Ed. C. Logue, London, Pan Books, 1980)
GUINEA FOWL	TARENTAAL (Totius, *Afrikaans Poems with English Translations*, O.U.P., 1962. Trans. Guy Butler)
	AKOSUA 'NOWA (Joe de Graft, *Messages, Poems from Ghana*, London: Heinemann, 1971)
HIPPO	DAWN HIPPO (Sydney Clouts, *Collected Poems*, Cape Town: David Philip, 1984)
	THE HIPPOPOTAMUS (Ogden Nash, *Collected Verse from 1929 on*, London: Dent)

THE HABITS OF THE HIPPOPOTAMUS (Arthur Guiterman from his *Lyric Laughter*, E.P. Dutton in *The Children's Book of Comic Verse*, Ed. C Logue. London: Pan Books, 1980)
THE HIPPOPOTAMUS (Hilaire Belloc, *Complete Verse*, London: Gerald Duckworth, 1970)
BELLOWING HIPPOPOTAMUS (Guy Butler, 'High Corner', 122 High Street, Grahamstown)
THE HIPPOPOTAMUS (Roy Macnab). (*Poems* by Roy Macnab and Douglas Reid Skinner, Cape Town: David Philip, 1981)
THE HIPPOPOTAMUS (T.S. Eliot, *Poems 1909-1925*), London: Faber & Faber, 1942)

HYENA   OLD TIKA (Kingsley Fairbridge, *Veld and Verse*, O.U.P., 1928)
WITCHCRAFT (Musaemura Zimunya) *Country Dawns and City Lights*, Harare: Longman Zimbabwe,1985)

IMPALA   HERD OF IMPALA (Colin Style, *Musical Saw*,Harare: Mopani Poets, No.6, Poetry Society of Rhodesia, 1981)

JACKAL   THE JACKAL'S LAMENT and KOROKEN THE JACKAL (Arthur Markowitz, *The Rebirth of the Ostrich*, Gaborone: National Museum and Art Gallery, 1971)
SHE-JACKAL (Douglas Livingstone, *Selected Poems*, Johannesburg: Donker, 1984)

KUKU   FOR A DEAD KUDU BULL (Hjalmar Thesen, *Poems*, Box 10, Knysna, N.D.)
ON CLOUDS (Douglas Livingstone, *Selected Poems*, Johannesburg: Donker, 1984)

LEOPARD   THE BLESSING (Bruce Hewett, *The Dawn of Song*, Grahamstown: New Coin, I.S.E.A.,1985)
LEOPARD (Charles Eglington, *Under the Horizon*, Cape Town: Purnell, 1977)
YELLOW EYES (Kingsley Fairbridge, *Veld Verse*, O.U.P., 1928)
A LEOPARD LIVES IN A MUU TREE (Jonathan Kariara, *Poems from East Africa*, London: Heinemann, 1976)

LION   THE LION (Hilaire Belloc, *Complete Verse*, London: Duckworth, 1970)
THE LION (Ogden Nash, *Collected Verse from 1929 on*, London: Dent, 1961)
LION AND SUN (Bruce Hewett, *The Dawn of Song*, Grahamstown: New Coin, I.S.E.A., 1985)
ANATOMY OF A LION (Colin Style, New Coin Poetry, March 1966, Vol.2, No.1)
BIRDS (Ruth Miller, *Selected Poems*, London: Chatto and Windus, The Hogarth Press, 1968)
THE LION AND GIRAFFE (Thomas Pringle, *Afar in the Desert and other S.A. Poems of South Africa* London: Longmans, 1881)
THE LIONESS AND HER CHILDREN (Arthur Markowitz, *The Rebirth of the Ostrich*, Gaborone: National Museum and Art Gallery, 1971)

LIZARD   LIZARD (Anne Yates, 94 Banbury Road, Oxford)

MANTIS   MANTIS (Ruth Miller, *Selected Poems*, London: Chatto and Windus, The Hogarth Press, 1968)
MANTIS (Robert Dederick, Grahamstown: ISEA. *New Coin Poetry*, Dec.1966, Vol.2, No.4)

MONKEY	PRIMATES (Rowland Molony, *Four Voices: Poetry from Zimbabwe*, Bulawayo: Books of Zimbabwe, 1982)
NAGAPIE	NAGAPIE (BUSHBABY) Wilma Stockenström, *(Van Vergetelheid en Glans*, Cape Town: Human & Rousseau, 1976. Trans. Guy Butler)
ORYX	KALAHARI ORYX (Hjalmar Thesen, *Poems*, Box 10, Knysna, N.D.)
OSTRICH	THE OSTRICH (Ogden Nash, *Collected Verse from 1929 on*, London: Dent, 1961)
	OSTRICH (Rowland Molony, from *Four Voices: Poetry from Zimbabwe*, Bulawayo: Books of Zimbabwe, 1982)
PORCUPINE	THE PORCUPINE (Hilaire Belloc, *Complete Verse*, London: Gerald Duckworth, 1970)
	ONE THAT WAS NEVER SEEN (Sydney Clouts, *Collected Poems*, Cape Town, David Philip, 1984)
	THE HUNTING OF THE PORCUPINE (Arthur Markowitz, *The Rebirth of the Ostrich*, Gaborone: National Museum and Art Gallery, 1971)
PUFF-ADDER	THE PUFF-ADDER (Kingsley Fairbridge, *Veld Verse*, O.U.P., 1928)
	LEVIATHAN (Douglas Livingstone, *Selected Poems*, Johannesburg: Donker, 1984)
QUAGGA	LEARNED OBITUARY (Guy Butler, 'High Corner', 122 High Street, Grahamstown)
RHINO	ZEUS RHINOCEROS (Sydney Clouts, *Collected Poems*, Cape Town, David Philip, 1984)
	RHINOCEROS (Harold Farmer, *The Mambo Book of Zimbabwean Verse in English*, Harare: Mambo Press, 1986)
	RHINOCEROS (Ogden Nash *Collected Verse*, London: Duckworth, 1972)
SCORPION	THE SCORPION (William Plomer, *Selected Poems*, Johannesburg: Donker, 1985)
	THE SCORPION (Hilaire Belloc, *Complete Verse*, London: Gerald Duckworth, 1970)
	A SHADE FOR SCORPIONS (Perseus Adams, *Grass for the Unicorn*, Cape Town: Juta, 1975)
SNAKE	THE SLITHERING MAMBA (Mordikai A. Hamutyinei, *The Mambo Book of Zimbabwean Verse in English*, Harare: Mambo Press, 1986)
	THE REDEEMER (Efua Sutherland, *Messages, Poems from Ghana*, London: Heinemann, 1971)
	THE SNAKE AND THE LIZARD (Rowland Molony, *Four Voices: Poetry from Zimbabwe*, Bulawayo: Books of Zimbabwe, 1982)
SPIDER	SPIDER (Ruth Miller, *Selected Poems*, London: Chatto & Windus, 1968)
	JUMPING SPIDER (Perseus Adams, *Grass for the Unicorn*, Cape Town: Juta, 1975)
	TARANTULA (Musaemura Zimunya, *Kingfisher, Tikinya and other Poems*, Harare: Longman Zimbabwe, 1982)
SPRINGBOK	SPRINGBOKS (From *The Trek*, XIII, F.G. Slater, *Collected Poems*, London: Blackwood, 1957)
TORTOISE	THE TORTOISE (Peter Strauss, *Bishop Bernward's Door*, Cape Town: David Philip, 1983)
	MOUNTAIN TORTOISE (Ernst van Heerden, Bergskilpad. Trans. Richard Harvey, *Afrikaans Poems with English Translations*, Cape Town, O.U.P., 1962)

276

	THE TORTOISE AND THE HARE (Berin N. Gilfillan (Hilton College) *English Alive*, 1979. SACEE, Box 216, Rondebosch, 7700)
UNICORN	THE SAILING OF THE ARK (C.S. Lewis, *Poems*, ed. Walter Hooper, London: Bles, 1964)
	GRASS FOR THE UNICORN (Perseus Adams, *Grass for the Unicorn*, Cape Town: Juta, 1975)
	THE UNICORN (Bruce Hewett, *The Dawn of Song*, Grahamstown: New Coin, I.S.E.A., 1985)
	THE UNICORN (Robert Greig, *Talking Bull*, Johannesburg: Bateleur Press, 1975)
VULTURE	BUSHVELD BALLET (Cythna Letty, *Children of the Hours*, Johannesburg: Donker, 1981)
	VULTURES (Patrick Cullinan, *Horizon Fifty Miles Away*, Silver Spring, Witteboomen, Hout Bay Road, Constantia, 7800)
	VULTURE (Douglas Livingstone, *Selected Poems*, Johannesburg: Donker, 1984)
	THE WOMAN WHO WAS A SISTER TO VULTURES (Arthur Markowitz, *The Rebirth of the Ostrich*, Gaborone: National Museum and Art Gallery, 1971)
WILDCAT	WHAT'S LEFT OF A WILDCAT? (Charl Cilliers, 13 Avoca Road, Rondebosch, 7700)
	GENTLING A WILDCAT (Douglas Livingstone, *Selected Poems* Johannesburg: Donker, 1984)
WILDEBEEST	ROCK ART (Douglas Livingstone, *The Anvil's Undertone*, Johannesburg: Donker, 1978)
XYLOCOPA	XYLOCOPA, The Carpenter Bee, or Zingizi, (Guy Butler, 122 High Street, Grahamstown)
YAHOO	A SCHOLARLY NOTE (Guy Butler, 122 High Street, Grahamstown)
ZEBRA	THE ZEBRAS (Roy Campbell, *Collected Works*, Johannesburg: Donker, 1985)
	ZEBRA (Stephen Gray, *It's About Time*, Mantis, Cape Town: David Philip, 1974)
	ZEBRA (Douglas Livingstone, *Selected Poems*, Johannesburg: Donker, 1986)
	THE CLAN PRAISES OF THE PEOPLE OF CHIHOTA'S CLAN (Recorded from Shona by A.C. Hodgson, *The Mambo Book of Zimbabwean Verse in English*, Harare: Mambo Press, 1986)

Sources of Pictures

1. Originals

Cover	Gordon Vorster
Ant	Lindy Huggins
Dragonfly	Lindy Huggins
Lizard	Leigh Voigt
Mantis	Cecil Skotnes
Nagapie	Lindy Huggins
Porcupine	Leigh Voigt
Rhino	Claire Gavronsky
Spider	Cecil Skotnes
Tortoise	Cecil Skotnes
Unicorn	Claire Gavronsky
Wildcat	Lindy Huggins
Xylocopa	Lindy Huggins
Yahoo	Lindy Huggins, after Arthur Rackham, *Gulliver's Travels*, London, 1906, and George Morrow, *Gulliver's Travels*, London, n.d.

2. Rock Paintings and Engravings

a. Printed Sources

BATTISS, W. et al.	*The Art of South Africa*, Pietermaritzburg: Shuter & Shooter, 1958
BLEEK, D.F.	*More Rock Paintings in South Africa*, London: Methuen, 1940
ROSENTHAL, GOODWIN & BLEEK	*Cave Artists of South Africa*, Cape Town: Balkema, 1953
RUDNER, Jalmar	*The Hunter and his Art*, Cape Town: Struik, 1970
STOW, G.W.	*Rock Paintings in South Africa*. Ed. D.F. Bleek. London: Methuen, 1930
SUMMERS, R. (ed.)	*Prehistoric Rock Art of the Federation of Rhodesia & Nyasaland*, London: Chatto & Windus, 1959
TONGUE, H.M.	*Bushman Paintings*, Oxford, 1909
TOWNLEY JOHNSON, R.	*Major Rock Paintings of Southern Africa*, Cape Town: David Philip, 1979
VINNICOMBE, P.	*People of the Eland*, Pietermaritzburg: Natal University Press, 1976
WILLCOX, A.R.	*The Rock Art of South Africa*, London: Nelson, 1963.
WILMAN, M.	*The Rock Engravings of Griqualand West*, Cambridge: 1933
WOODHOUSE, Bert	*When Animals Were People*, Johannesburg: Chris van Rensburg Publications, 1984

278

b. Copies (by Lindy Huggins — except where otherwise stated.)

Bushmen Hunters: *Summers,* (Sue Ross)
African attacking Bushman: *Townley Johnson,* (Sue Ross)
White Men on Horses, and Wagons: *Townley Johnson,* (Sue Ross)

Antbear	*Summers,* Plate 13. Chinamora Reserve, Makumbe Cave.
Baboon	*Bleek,* Plate 25.
Buffalo	*Summers,* Plate 12. Mrewe Cave.
Chameleon	*Rudner,* Plate 6. Aigub Rock, Brandberg.
Cheetah	*Woodhouse,* p24, (Redrawn by Sue Ross)
Cobra	*Rosenthal,* No. 33. Hermanspoort, Kleinfontein.
Duiker	*Summers,* Plate 70. Nswatugi Cave, Matopos.
Eland	*P. Vinnicombe,* Frontispiece, *Piece of the Eland.*
Elephant	(1) *Tongue,* No. 92.
	(2) *Wilman,* Plate 29.
Frog	*Stow,* Plate 45.
Giraffe	*Summers,* Engraving, Beit Bridge Area, on a tributary of the Metengwe River.
Hippo	*Tongue,* No. 6.
Impala	*Bleek,* Plate 17.
Jackal	*Wilman,* Plate 30. Niekerk's Hoop, Hay.
Kudu	*Summers,* Plate 4. Robert MacIlwaine Park.
Leopard	(1) *Tongue,* No. 11.
	(2) *Rosenthal,* Plate 40. Longreach, Lower Black Kei, Cape.
Lion	*Summers,* Plate 63. Line drawing. White Rhino Shelter, Matopos.
Oryx	*Rudner,* Gemsbok in black and faded red from the Okapi Rock, Brandberg.
Ostrich	*Bleek,* Plate 21.
Quagga	*Wilman,* Plate 23.
Rhino	*Tongue,* No. 99.
Snake	*Townley Johnson,* Plate 51. (Redrawn by Sue Ross)
Springbok	*Townley Johnson,* Plate 102. (Redrawn by Sue Ross)
Vulture	*Woodhouse* p103. Abel's Cave, Cockscombe Mountain, C.P.
Wildebeeste	*Wilman,* Plate 27. Black Wildebeeste.
Zebra	*Woodhouse,* p117. (Redrawn by Sue Ross)

OTHERS

Introduction

Map of Africa	R.V. Tooley: *Collectors' Guide to Maps of the African Continent,* London, 1969
Etosha Pan Wild Life	Lino-cut by John N. Muafangejo.

Hunting the Giraffe and Zebra & Wildebeeste	W. Cornwallis Harris: *The Wild Sports of Southern Africa*, London, 1839.
Hunters and Lions	R. Gordon Cumming: *A Hunter's Life in South Africa*, London, 1850.
Group of Animals by River	David Livingstone: *Missionsreisen und Forschungen in Sud Africa*, Leipzig, 1858, v.2.

Animals

Crocodile	Wooden Carving. Pokerwork, Basotho. W. Battiss et al. *The Art of South Africa*, Shuter & Shooter, 1958. Redrawn by Lindy Huggins.
Eagle	After a drawing by Harold Rubin. Redrawn by Lindy Huggins.
Frogs	Wooden Carving. Fort Hare Museum. Redrawn by Lindy Huggins.
Giraffe	Roy Campbell, from *Light on a Dark Horse*. London: Hollis & Carter, 1969, p.13a.
Giraffe and Groom	Chinese Silk Painting. *China's Discovery of Africa*, London: Arthur B. Probsthain, 1949. Redrawn by Lindy Huggins.
Guinea-Fowl	H.A. Aschenborn, Etching, 'Moonlight'. Pretoria Art Museum.
Hare	Edward Topsell, *History of Four-footed Beasts*. London, 1607.
Hyena	After Fritz Krampe (1913-1966). Johannesburg Art Gallery. Redrawn by Lindy Huggins.
Monkey	E. Caldwell, from Percy FitzPatrick, *Jock of the Bushveld*, London, 1907.
Puffadder	From Rev. J.C. Wood, *Illustrated Natural History*. London, 1862.
Scorpion	Edward Topsell, *History of Serpents*. London, 1608.
Unicorn	Anonymous.
Vulture	Linocut, Azaria Mpatha, *Contrast*, July 1983, Vol. 14, No. 7.

Sources of Proverbs

Our main sources are:

SECHUANA
PLAATJE, Solomon T.
Sechuana Proverbs with Literal Translations and their European Equivalents, London: Kegan Paul, 1916.

SHONA
KRIEL, Abraham
An African Horizon: Ideals in Shona lore & literature, Cape Town: U.C.T., 1971.

XHOSA
SOGA, John Henderson
The South Eastern Bantu, Johannesburg, 1930.
The Ama-Xhosa: life and customs, Lovedale, 1931.

ZULU
NYEMBEZI, Cyril Lincoln
Zulu Proverbs, Johannesburg: University of the Witwatersrand Press, 1954.

BUSHMEN
WOODHOUSE, Bert
When Animals were People, Johannesburg: Chris van Rensburg, 1984.

FOLKLORE
PARTRIDGE, A.C.
Folklore of Southern Africa, Cape Town: Purnell, 1973.